MAGIC
SHOP

JACQUELINE RICHARDS

THE
MAGIC
SHOP

HELEN GRAHAM

RIDER

LONDON SYDNEY AUCKLAND JOHANNESBURG

First published in 1992 by Rider,
An imprint of Random Century Group Ltd,
20 Vauxhall Bridge Road, London SW1V 2SA

Random Century Group Australia (Pty) Ltd
20 Alfred Street, Milsons Point,
Sydney, NSW 2061, Australia

Random Century New Zealand Ltd,
18 Poland Road, Glenfield,
Auckland 10, New Zealand

Random Century Group South Africa (Pty) Ltd,
PO Box 337, Bergvlei 2012, South Africa

Typeset by Tek Art Ltd, Addiscombe, Croydon, Surrey
Printed and bound in Great Britain by
Mackays of Chatham PLC, Chatham, Kent

A catalogue record for this book is available
from the British Library.

ISBN 0 7126 5384 8

This book is printed on recycled paper.

CONTENTS

Preface   *vii*

1   Letting Go of Tensions   1

2   Making Time for Health and Healing   28

3   Mobilising the Healing Power of Imagery   51

4   Recognising Health Needs   70

5   Actualising Personal Powers and Potentials   88

6   Cultivating Healthy Attitudes   105

7   Influencing the Healing Process   120

8   Acknowledging Painful Messages   141

9   Tuning in to Inner Wisdom and Guidance   158

10 Directing Subtle Energies   176

11 Listening to the Wisdom of the Body   192

References and further reading   214

Index   219

PREFACE

THE PURPOSE OF THIS BOOK

A few years ago a colleague and I offered a short residential course on psychological approaches in healing to National Health Service personnel which recruited nationally and proved successful. Subsequently I was asked to run a similar but extended course in a large regional psychiatric hospital and to contribute to staff training in a general hospital in the north of England. Before agreeing to do so I decided to 'test' the material on a wider audience. An eleven-week course on psychological healing was therefore offered to the general public through the auspices of Keele University's Department of Adult and Continuing Education.

The response was quite unprecedented and overwhelming, so much so that the initial course had to run several evenings a week to cope with the record numbers attracted.

Interest in the subject has shown little sign of diminishing over the years. Indeed, quite the opposite would seem to be the case. It is simply not possible to offer sufficient courses to meet the increasing demand. For a number of years I have run two evening courses, augmented by weekend workshops, concurrently each term. These are held in four different venues in three counties, with some people travelling considerable distances to attend, and many following the course two, or even three times. Necessarily the course evolved, if only to meet the needs of those who attended more than once. Its content shifted from informal lectures on and discussion of different psychological approaches to healing illustrated with practical exercises, to a linked series of experiential workshops, each introduced by relevant theory, research and practice, and followed by discussion.

In response to requests for relevant reading material, I wrote a sourcebook, *Time, Energy and the Psychology of*

Healing, which details and discusses theory, practice and research relevant to all aspects of the psychology of healing. However, the need most commonly expressed by course members is for a book that sets out the workshop exercises, enabling them to be practised at home and at leisure and shared with others. The present book attempts to meet this need, and to introduce a wider audience to exercises which can be used to help them to relax, to develop awareness of themselves physically, mentally and spiritually, and to apply these insights in the maintenance of health and the prevention and treatment of illness.

WHOM THE BOOK IS FOR

I never ask participants their reasons for attending my courses and workshops because I regard this as intrusive and inconsistent with approaches to healing that are non-invasive. This apparent lack of curiosity comes as a surprise to some, but is a relief to many for whom it takes a good deal of courage simply to attend, much less explain themselves. Nevertheless people frequently declare their reasons for attending, either privately to me or publicly to the other group members. As might be expected, some of those attending are ill, often seriously, with cancers, heart conditions, multiple sclerosis, rheumatoid arthritis, myalgic encephalomyelitis and auto-immune diseases. Some suffer persistent pain. Others have dependants, relatives or friends who are sick, terminally ill or disabled; while others have persistent health problems that may not be serious but are irritating or moderately disabling (for example allergies, headache, migraine, skin conditions, insomnia). Some suffer from stress-related disorders such as hypertension, gastro-intestinal disorders or ulcers. Others have a history of emotional or psychological problems: chronic anxieties, phobias or depression.

Of the above some are desperate, having been told there is nothing more that orthodox medicine can do for them, or that they must learn to live with their conditions.

Others are dissatisfied and disillusioned with orthodox medical approaches, especially medication, and wish to explore alternatives. Some of those dismayed by the short-comings of the National Health Service, or the prospect of its dissolution, are determined to minimise their dependence on it or private medicine through self-help and preventative strategies. Others wish to gain greater understanding of the psychological factors they recognise as a component of their own illnesses or those of others. A number have been introduced to psychological approaches (for example in the treatment of illnesses such as cancer, in stress-management programmes, or through reading) and wish to sustain or develop them.

Many people do not have health or health-related problems as such but suffer from what might be regarded as 'problems in living'. These include occupational stress and various life crises; marital, family, personal, interpersonal or professional difficulties; and coming to terms with divorce, loneliness, loss or bereavement. The last typically includes those grieving for aborted, miscarried or stillborn babies and for children who have died in infancy or later childhood from disabling conditions, accidents, murder or neglect. Some are grieving the 'lost' lives of children born with handicaps, and some the loss of their own life – on receipt of a terminal diagnosis.

Nevertheless, people with 'problems' comprise a relatively small proportion of those who attend. Some have no particular problem, but a feeling that they could be getting more out of life. Many more have a professional interest in the subject. They include nurses, physiotherapists, health visitors, community psychiatric nurses, social workers, students of psychology and, increasingly, medical practitioners; healers in unorthodox or complementary fields such as reflexology, acupuncture, hypnotherapy, art, drama and music therapies, herbalism, homeopathy, aromatherapy; spiritual and clairvoyant healers; and professional counsellors looking to broaden their existing skills.

Increasingly there are stress-management consultants and people organising or involved in self-help and support groups (for sufferers of tinnitus, agoraphobia, cancer, cystic fibrosis, child abuse, etc.), or those wishing to work in these areas. A good many are seeking stress management for themselves, or are looking for a career change, or an occupation following retirement. An increasing number are school teachers who find relaxation and stress-management procedures valuable in dealing with staff/student problems and class-room control, and imagery useful in stimulating creativity and self-expression in pupils. A small but growing number of participants are in the leisure industry, involved in fitness and health programmes in sports, leisure and health centres.

Finally, there are those who attend simply out of interest or curiosity, for a change of routine, or a chance to relax and enjoy themselves and meet other people.

As will become clear from the illustrative examples provided, there are more women than men on the courses, the female-male ratio being in the order of 3 or 4 to 1, but the number of males attending is increasing with each course.

HOW TO USE THIS BOOK

The exercises in this book are set out in a progressive sequence so that each builds upon those before it. Nevertheless they each stand alone as complete in themselves. Every exercise is introduced with pertinent information, including some explanation of its aims, purpose and relevance to health in the broadest sense, and followed by a brief commentary on the issues it typically highlights, illustrated with observations drawn from 'real life' experience of working with groups and individuals and the questions they commonly ask. References and suggestions for further reading – mostly available from local libraries and good bookshops – are provided at the end of the book.

The directions for some of the exercises are rather lengthy. It is therefore recommended that, initially at least, someone reads them to you, or that you record them on audiotape, leaving pauses where necessary, until you have memorised them and are able to forego external aids. The directions have been written explicitly for this purpose.

It is also recommended that you keep a record of your experiences. This is because some of the insights and awarenesses that occur are quickly forgotten – rather like many dreams – and certain features recur in different contexts and in different detail in the course of the exercises, so that what initially may appear obscure, meaningless or trivial becomes progressively more clear, intelligible and relevant. The record may take the form of a written 'log' or an audiotape. The latter has the advantage of greater immediacy and speed, and of affording greater detail, but may not always be convenient. This record can also be used to detail experiences and insights which occur *as a result* of the exercises rather than during them. For example, a feature or theme arising in an exercise may recur or be amplified in a subsequent dream, reverie or actual life experience. 'Coincidences' such as these are invariably highly significant, but are frequently overlooked or dismissed. A 'log' helps to highlight interrelationships in one's life; to identify significant issues or 'themes' that emerge; to 'jog' memories; to indicate stages in the development of greater self-awareness; and, importantly, to cultivate a certain discipline in the study of oneself. Those who feel knowledge of others' responses will affect their experience of the exercises are advised to refrain from reading the commentary sections until after completing and recording the details of each exercise.

1

LETTING GO OF TENSIONS

*Come unto me all ye that labour and are heavy
laden, and I will give you rest.*

Matthew 11:8

Welcome to the Magic Shop. You may be wondering what
it is, and what, if anything, magic has to do with healing,
imaginative or otherwise. In fact it has everything to do with
it, because the art of healing throughout all ages and parts of
the world is rooted in magic.

You may find this difficult to accept if you associate magic
with stage performers and tend to dismiss it as entertaining
nonsense; and even more so if you associate it with Satanism
and evil. However, magic may be more properly thought of
as practical or applied mysticism.

Magic and mysticism

The term mysticism derives from the Greek work *muo*, which
means to close in the sense of to complete something. A
mystic is literally a person who has a complete view of the
universe, or cosmic vision, and therefore perceives its
relations and understands its laws and principles. These
visionaries who see the true nature of reality assert that the
world of ordinary everyday perception is but a fragment of
a far greater, infinite, indivisible and ultimately indescribable
universe, the parts of which are all interrelated and inter-
dependent. Fundamentally, therefore, the universe is one,
with no part or parts separate from any other. Everything
that exists within it is an expression of an underlying unity
which subsists through all phenomena, including man, whose

1

very essence or soul is a replica of this greater universe – a microcosm of the macrocosm. However, knowledge of this greater reality is concealed from normal awareness, which is confined to what is immediately apparent, and beyond ordinary comprehension. Knowledge of this hidden or occult reality comes only by way of revelation, insight or intuition, which is sudden, penetrative and certain beyond all doubt. Mysticism is therefore concerned with the development of enhanced perception, awareness and sensitivity, which enables the individual to apprehend ultimate reality directly, and thereby penetrate the mysteries of the universe and work with its forces. Magic or sorcery is the ability to use this understanding of the fundamental forces of nature to create effects in the world.

There are indications in various teachings passed down through history and in ancient documents that early man was inherently attuned to the magical, in that he instinctively and collectively understood and lived in accordance with natural laws. However, it would appear that this non-verbal, intuitive awareness of the wholeness of things and the relations between all phenomena is a feature of pre-literate cultures, which is superseded as the parts of the brain specialised for language and language-related functions evolve and dominate those parts of the brain more specialised for non-verbal, holistic, intuitive processes. Therefore, as a result of his intellectual evolution, instinctual magical awareness has largely been lost by man and is retained by only a few individuals.

Traditionally it is to these visionaries who perceive the overall pattern and harmony of the universe that others have turned with their questions. Thus in every culture throughout the world masters of the occult have tended to control access to knowledge, in so far as they decided what was to be disclosed and to whom, and the means of dissemination. They were therefore the first educators, and arguably all knowledge is rooted in their wisdom, although the full extent of this remains unknown.

The abilities attributed to those who applied this knowledge in order to influence worldly events and human destiny include directing the weather and climate, by making rain, for example; influencing crop growth; divining the future; telepathy; clairvoyance; and healing. Healers used natural forces, herbs, plants and animals; minerals, crystals, precious and semi-precious stones; symbols and shapes; and knowledge of the principles of colour, light and sound. It has been suggested that the magicians and sorcerors who practised these arts were actually applying scientific laws which are, for the most part, still unrecognized by contemporary science. Certainly much of this knowledge has been lost to Western culture, although there is clear evidence that it existed.

The remarkable powers concentrated in the pyramids of Egypt have only recently been recognised, and are still not fully appreciated or understood. Indeed the means by which the pyramids were constructed remains uncertain. According to legend, the ancients of Egypt and of Central and South America could by knowledge of sound alone split massive stone slabs along precise harmonic lines and move them into position by resonance. The temples of Uxmal and Machu Picchu are thought by some to have been raised and patterned in this way. Legend also has it that much of the wisdom of the ancients is stored in the Great Pyramid of Giza, although this has yet to be discovered or deciphered. Irrespective of the truth of these legends, it appears that much of the arcane knowledge of the ancient Egyptians passed down into ancient Greece, the acknowledged source of Western culture.

There can be little doubt that the thinking of Pythagorus, Heraclitus, Empedocles and other Greek philosophers and sages is mystical in origin, as is that of Hippocrates, who is widely regarded as the father of Western medicine. However, by the end of the Classical period in Greece the development of rationalism had obscured the mystic vision from which the knowledge of the ancients was derived. Thus overshadowed by developments in thought, magic and its practices then came under attack from Christianity. Based as they were on pagan principles that assert the powers and potentials of the individual, and encourage their development, they were seen as a threat, not only to the institution of the Church, but to its concept of an external, all-powerful God. Visionary

3

movements, including the Bogomils, Albigenses, Rosicrucians, Cathars and Freemasons, were deemed heretical and were systematically persecuted. The Church has thus been justifiably accused of bringing about the Dark Ages of medicine, because the healing arts of the ancients were purged, to be replaced by often brutal practices such as flagellation. Nevertheless, although fragmented and obscured, their wisdom was not lost completely, but was passed down through the ages in secret oral tradition by a number of magical orders, fraternities and sororities.

Magic and medicine

By the Middle Ages the repositories of the ancient wisdom throughout the Anglo-Saxon world were the wise women known as witches, who, arguably, were the most advanced scientists of the period, acting in the long-standing pagan tradition of magic. They were primarily medical practitioners, and Paracelsus (1493–1541), the distinguished physician and founder of modern chemistry, attributed his understanding of the laws and practices of medicine to them (Achterberg, 1985, and Webster, 1988). However, as purveyors of magic they were subjected to the most intense and systematic purges by the Church, in which around 1 million women are estimated to have been tortured and killed. This had dire consequences for healing within Western culture because there was subsequently no serious study or practice of medicine until the eighteenth century. Indeed, documents relating to the witch trials provide the only evidence of healing practices throughout this period, but from what little is known it would appear that these were consistent with those of tribes throughout Europe and Asia.

During the seventeenth century the Russians discovered tribes throughout Siberia, among whom specialists in magic were termed *shaman* or *haman*. The magical powers attributed to them included mastery of natural lore, healing the sick, telepathy, clairvoyance, divination of the future, dream interpretation, mastery of fire, rain-making, and ascent into the heavens and descent into the underworld, where they communicated with spirits on behalf of the members of their

4

community. The attempts of the witches to use natural forces in healing, their use of spells and 'flight' on broomsticks is clearly within this shamanic tradition, which subsequent archeological evidence has shown to be some 20,000 years old, very widespread and remarkably similar throughout the world. This tradition still exists in the present time and is well documented in anthropological literature and research.

Anthropological literature suggests that the magical 'flights' of the shaman occur in the imagination or unconscious, and that they are therefore 'flights of fantasy'. Shamanic techniques are essentially a means of accessing, exploring and interpreting what may be thought of as the landscapes of the human mind. Shamans recognise the imagination as a function of what modern man calls the 'unconscious mind', and know that its contents – images – often reveal and verify inner conditions hidden to ordinary consciousness. Accordingly these images are often indicative of the way individuals perceive themselves and their world, and as such provide significant cues to their emotional and physical health and susceptibility to illness. Through elucidation of the imagery produced in dreams, day-dreams, fantasy and reverie, shamans often discern factors, such as fears, anxieties and concerns, which have given rise to psychological or physical illness in an individual, and gain insight into the appropriate treatment. Shamans can therefore be regarded as adepts of 'imaginative medicine'.

IMAGINATION

Although somewhat obscured within orthodox Western medicine, the central role of the imagination in health, sickness and cure is none the less discernible. It is now widely accepted that images are often instrumental in setting up the conditions in which illness can become established. This is evident with regard to stress, which is now acknowledged as a contributory factor in the development of disease, as we shall see later in our discussion of how the imagination can fuel anxiety.

The human organism responds physiologically to stressful events and circumstances in a manner which enables it to deal with them – that is by mobilising it for action. This involves increases in blood pressure, pulse and heart rate, muscular tension, blood sugar, hormone and cholesterol levels in the blood, and the inhibition of non-essential vegetative and digestive functions. Clearly if you are faced with a rampaging bull it is more important to be able to deal with it in some way than to digest what may be your last meal. These responses are normal, healthy and necessary to our survival in dangerous or life-threatening situations. They become unhealthy and life threatening only if they become habitual and sustained. They then take a severe toll on bodily functions leading to hypertension and to increased risk of major organ failure – stroke, kidney and coronary heart disease.

This has led to widespread concern about stress, which is often seen, quite wrongly, as some*thing* which affects everyone to an equal degree. However, this is not the case. Many people would find it extremely stressful to be required to drink 8–10 pints of fluid one after the other. Yet others frequently drink this amount of beer and lager in an evening and find it extremely pleasurable. Indeed they might be quite distressed if prevented from doing so. Similarly some people view the idea of jumping from an aeroplane suspended only by a sheet of flimsy material and a few ropes with absolute horror, while others consider it to be fun. For this reason it makes little sense to speak of stress as such, and so current thinking favours the idea of stressors – those events or circumstances that individuals perceive as stressful.

Many stressors reside wholly or partly within the imagination. Fears, anxieties and dread are often responses to our worst imaginings, rather than to actual happenings, and many of them relate not to life-threatening or dangerous issues but to everyday, ordinary events. Thus we may fear that no-one likes us; that we will fail examinations or job interviews; that we will suffer excruciating pain during dental treatment; that we or our loved ones will be involved in an aircrash or traffic pile-up, and so on.

These fears translate into physiological responses which can give rise to so-called 'stress-related' diseases – stroke, heart attack, ulcers, gastro-intestinal problems, kidney failure

– and contribute to many more, including what is now termed the 'post-traumatic stress syndrome'. Indeed, it is now estimated that 75 per cent of all medical conditions are stress related. Furthermore, the award of £34,000 damages by the British High Court in December 1990 to firemen for 'psychological injury' sustained in the underground fire at King's Cross station in London establishes in law the principle that psychological factors can give rise to physical illness.

Having thus established the conditions in which illness may arise, the imagination may then foster the development of disease. This can happen in a number of ways. For example, someone may wake up in the morning with a slightly sore throat. Although it is not particularly severe, he immediately becomes anxious that it may become really painful, especially as he has a day's work to get through before an important evening engagement. All of these events are imaginary in the sense that they are not at that time reality, but the anxiety about them is real, and has direct physiological effects.

The term anxiety derives from the latin *angustia*, meaning 'narrowing', which describes fairly accurately its effects on the throat and chest, which constrict, restricting swallowing and breathing. The person may then remember that his uncle died of a throat cancer, the first sign of which was a sore throat, and as he begins to imagine the worst, his anxiety increases, his throat tightens further, and by the evening he is in pain and unable to attend his engagement.

Many of the images that 'fuel' the imagination are ready-made, provided by the medical profession, government health statistics and the mass media, so medical diagnoses often conjure specific images and expectations about the course of a given illness and probable outcomes. The common image of cancer is that it is a powerful disease, but cancer specialist Carl Simonton observes that in fact the cancer cell is not strong but weak. Although larger than normal, cancer cells are sluggish and confused, and rather than attacking or invading – of which they are incapable – they simply overproduce. Nevertheless, cancer is generally viewed as 'deadly', even though a high proportion of cancers

7

are curable, and 30–40 per cent of people who develop them recover and have no recurrence of the condition. The very word 'cancer' is so alarming to some people that they cannot even bring themselves to utter it, and so describe those persons with cancer as suffering from 'CA'.

AIDS has a similarly bad image, which fails to accommodate both long-term survivors and those who have reversed blood tests from HIV positive to negative.

In some cases this imagery can determine life or death independently of any medical intervention. These images differ from culture to culture, so while in Britain the bowels are believed to be a major factor in illness and are commonly diagnosed as such, the French imagine the liver to be of particular importance and are significantly more likely to diagnose it as the source of illness, and the Germans are more likely to attribute disease to problems of the heart and circulation.

Research evidence suggests that people who do not share these images do not succumb to illness at the same rate. Hence the mentally handicapped have a significantly lower incidence of cancers than the population as a whole; and cancer is virtually unknown among catatonic schizophrenics who have totally withdrawn themselves from society and its expectations.

The power of the imagination is particularly relevant to the experience of pain. Psychological research suggests that pain is often suffered because it is expected – that is, it relies to a considerable extent on the beliefs, expectations and imaginings of the person concerned. All the indications are that the opportunity to imagine the effects of a 'painful' stimulus generally guarantees a painful response which may not be experienced otherwise. Indeed, this is the basic principle of torture.

The imagination thus often works to produce undesirable outcomes, but it can work to the individual's advantage as well. The surgeon Bernie Siegel (1990, p.96) relates the story of the cardiologist Bernard Lown who was

> on his rounds with his students when he pointed out a
> critically ill patient who had what he called 'a wholesome,

very loud third-sound gallop' to his heart. In medical terminology a gallop rhythm means that the heart is badly damaged and dilated. There was nothing further to be done for this man, and little hope for his recovery. None the less he did make an amazing return to health, and explained why some months later. As soon as he heard Dr Lown describe his heart as having a 'wholesome gallop', he said, he figured that meant it had a strong kick to it, like a horse, and he then became optimistic about his condition and knew that he would recover – which he did.

Orthodox medical practitioners quite deliberately exploit the power of the imagination in their use of placebos – 'fake' substances whose effects have been demonstrated to be as, or more effective than, real medications. However, it is also recognised that the prescription slip itself, rather than what is written on it, is often the vital ingredient in recovery. To the patient, this piece of paper with its apparently unbreakable code, is often a certificate of assured recovery, the doctor's promise of restored health.

But the doctor himself is the most powerful placebo of all, in that the chances of successful treatment seem to be directly proportional to the quality of the patient's relationship with him – in other words, to the extent that the patient imagines the doctor's interventions will be effective.

Despite the imagination's implicit role in health, illness and cure, orthodox medicine has given it insufficient attention until relatively recently. Increasingly, however, it is being obliged to do so as the importance of the imagination is demonstrated by medical and psychological research.

The purpose of the Magic Shop is to evoke the store of images within the individual in order to stimulate the 'magic' of their mind, and develop this potential for self-healing. This is achieved, in the ages-old manner of the shamans, by way of relaxation, which not only facilitates the production of imagery but is facilitated by it.

RELAXATION

Shamans evoke images in a number of ways. The healers of ancient Egypt and Greece, for example, frequently required their patients to sleep overnight in dream sanctuaries. Then, by shifting their awareness from its ordinary, rational, conscious mode to a non-ordinary intuitive, unconscious mode, the shamans are able to intuit the significance of the imagery thus produced. Typically, shamans also induce in their patients a state often described as trance-like or hypnotic, which facilitates, and is facilitated by, the production of imagery. This trance-like state is achieved in a variety of ways, including the use of drugs and alcohol, ritual movements, dance, chanting, drum music and meditation.

From the rational perspective of contemporary Western culture these rituals and their results may appear bizarre and alarming, and this view is reinforced by the tendency of recent years to label the experiences 'altered state of consciousness'. However, when scrutinised more closely, what is common to these states, however they are induced, is profound relaxation of normal modes of thinking and being in both the healer and patient.

Those who regard relaxation as slumping in front of the television or having a few drinks with friends may find this hard to accept. However, for most people relaxation is an altered state of consciousness in that it is an integrated shift in physiological functions which is rarely, if ever, achieved without training and practice. It is possible for a person to lie quietly on a couch for several hours, apparently relaxed, and still show no appreciable change in physiological functions. Signs of mental activity, physical excitement and anxiety may be evident, together with fidgety, restless movements and startled reactions to sudden noise. After 'rest' such as this people frequently fail to feel refreshed and retain symptoms of fatigue. Moreover, if watching television while resting, they may well show increased blood pressure and overall arousal.

Even when the person feels fairly relaxed there are often clinical signs of residual tension such as irregular breathing, increased pulse rate, involuntary or local reflexes such as wrinkling of the forehead, tension in the muscles of the face and swallowing.

In true relaxation tension is absent, breathing loses its irregularity, pulse rate drops, the throat relaxes and the person lies quietly with flaccid limbs, no visible traces of stiffness, no reflex swallowing and motionless, toneless eyelids.

Relaxation such as this has long been recognised as the opposite of nervous hypertension, which is a feature of many conditions such as insomnia, cough, palpitations, sudden pains, tremor, convulsions, digestive problems, diabetes, kidney disease, asthma, nephritis, heart conditions, arteriosclerosis, functional nervous disorders and obstetrical complications. It also occurs in the guise of symptoms, causes or effects throughout almost the entire range of medical practice and surgery. Relaxation has therefore been seen as an antidote which increases general resistance to infections and other noxious agents, decreases blood pressure and strain on the heart, and diminishes energy output and bodily movement thus preventing further strain or injury. Accordingly it has been prescribed in the treatment of numerous conditions, notably hypertension, insomnia, anxiety neuroses, heart conditions, hypochondria, stuttering and stammering, fatigue, exhaustion and sleep disturbance, toxic goitre, alimentary spasm, mucous colitis, peptic ulcer and chronic pulmonary tuberculosis, as well as in preparation for, and after, surgery.

Traditionally various means have been used to promote rest, although doctors now most frequently employ sedative drugs. Even so, patients often fail to derive its full benefits, especially in hospitals where ward routines are typically put before the patient's need for peace and quiet.

Advising a person to rest or relax is in itself quite futile because most people simply don't know how to. Their attempts to do so may even prove to be counterproductive as their restlessness may be increased by distress and vice versa.

Normally people are unaware that their muscles are tense and cannot judge accurately whether or not relaxation has been achieved. What is customarily called rest or relaxation is thus in many instances inadequate, which accounts for the failure of many so-called 'rest' cures. A person can only begin to relax when they know what tension is and how they produce it. Relaxation therefore involves the individual learning to identify tension in muscle groups by contracting or tightening them, and then ceasing to do so. This helps the

11

individual to realise that relaxation is not a doing, but is simply a non-doing, and that if they can tighten a muscle they can just as easily 'undo' it. Relaxation is essentially the cultivation of bodily awareness or muscle sense, and in principle it can be taught to anyone, providing they are willing, motivated to learn and practise, and able to follow instructions.

Even so, residual tension disappears only gradually and relaxation is slow and progressive rather than sudden and immediate. Most methods of relaxation therefore aim to produce progressively an extreme degree of neuro-muscular relaxation and to train the body to react in the desired manner as and when required. For this to be achieved regular practice is required. Moreover the process is initially rather lengthy. However, it can be simplified or shortened in a number of ways, by restricting training to a few muscle groups, for example.

When someone is able to relax muscles as quickly as tighten them, he can be taught to scan the body for tension and to concentrate on relaxing only those muscles. It is then possible to use everyday events such as traffic signals, radio or television bulletins and workshift bells as signals to scan and relax muscles. It is also possible to learn how to identify and relax the muscles not required in the performance of a task, while achieving a minimum of tension in those that are.

It follows from what has been stated previously that for most people the instruction 'relax' is meaningless. Therefore the following exercise avoids use of the term and focuses instead on the contrast between tightening of muscles – which most people find easy – and 'letting go' of this tension. Although apparently lengthy the exercise can easily be completed in under 20 minutes.

Exercise 1
Progressive relaxation augmented by imagery

Find somewhere you can sit or lie with a reasonable degree of comfort. If too comfortable you are likely to drift into sleep (which is why seated postures are recommended in many relaxation procedures), whereas if too uncomfortable or cold you are unlikely to sustain the motivation to achieve relaxation. Having done this, simply be aware of how your body is located in relation to its surroundings. Then close your eyes, or if this is not possible because of organic impairment or surgery, or difficult because of contact lenses, focus on a fixed point or object within your line of vision, such as a mark on a wall, ceiling or floor.

Then gradually draw your attention from your surroundings, and bring it to the boundary between your body and adjacent surfaces. As you do so, notice whether the contact is uncomfortable or painful, and adjust your position so as to maximise comfort and minimise pain. You may find that you need to remove restrictive clothing, shoes, jewelry or spectacles. At any point during the exercise when you feel the need to adjust your position to reduce discomfort or pain, do so.

When you are positioned as comfortably as possible, turn your attention to your feelings. How *do* you feel? Do you feel silly, or guilty about taking time to do the exercise?

How self-conscious are you? Are you worried about being seen by others, or, if doing this exercise in company, by their proximity, and your or their body smells or sounds? Are you worried about falling asleep or snoring, or because you may not be able to 'do' the exercise? Your reactions may reflect some of the basic anxieties of your life, and relate to some of the tensions you encounter as you proceed with the exercise. If during any part of the exercise thoughts, feelings, memories or impressions come to mind, make a mental note of them as these may have similar significance.

Now bring your attention to your toes. Without moving the overall position of your feet, push your toes down and away from you, as far as they will go, noticing as you do so the effect of this movement on the rest of your feet and legs. Sustain this action until you can identify the extent of its effects throughout your body, and then let go. Repeat this movement three times, or as many times as is necessary for you to become aware of its full implications for the rest of your body. When you have done this, flex your toes upwards and towards you as far as you can, and sustain the action until you can feel its effects not only locally in your feet and legs, but also in more distant areas of your body. Then simply let go. Repeat the action three times.

Now rotate each foot through 360 degrees, first in one direction, then the other, noticing any grinds, clicks or other noises and accompanying sensations. Then let go, and for a few moments simply experience the sensations in your feet and legs.

It is important to recognise the sensation of 'letting go' in contrast to that of tightening, and how both are achieved. The actions are sustained in order to enhance awareness of how muscle tension is achieved in a given muscle group, and the effects it has on other parts of the body. This may highlight habitual tensions and pain, and prompt awareness of the situations in which these typically occur. The movements therefore have implications for the mind/body system as a whole, and have particular relevance to the phenomenon of 'referred' pain, so through these exercises it may be possible to understand how the big toe, for example, can effect pain elsewhere in the body.

Now, bring your attention to your thighs, and press them firmly downwards against the chair or floor, noting the extent of this action throughout your body. When you have identified the furthest point of influence, let go. Then repeat the action three times.

Then, without moving the overall position of your legs, draw your inner thighs together, and hold them, once again noticing the effects of this movement on the rest of your body before letting go. Repeat this three times.

Now bring your attention to your buttocks and press down as hard as you can against the adjacent surface. As you are doing so ask yourself what in life you might bear down on, or in what situations this action seems familiar. Then let go. Repeat the action three times, noting its effect throughout the body. Then draw in or 'dimple' the sides of your buttocks and sustain the action until you are aware of its implications for the remainder of your body, then let go. Repeat three times.

When you have done this, allow your legs and feet to 'flop' and take a few seconds to become aware of the sensations within them. If you encounter any residual tension work on it by tightening and letting go of the relevant muscles and allow the latter sensation to generalise or spread throughout your lower limbs.

Having done this bring your attention to your lower back. Without shifting your overall position push it against the adjacent surface and hold it there, noting its implications for the rest of your body. This is particularly important given that the lower back is a major stress point where bodily tensions typically manifest, and that back problems are one of the chief causes of lost work days. Then let go and repeat three times. As you do so, ask yourself whether you generally feel that you have your back to the wall, or feel 'up against' things.

Now push your lower back forward as far as you can, arching it, and holding this action until you can feel its effects throughout your body. Before you let go, ask yourself whether you have ever been described as 'arch' in manner, or whether you frequently get your 'back up', and if so, about what. Then repeat the action three times. You may recognise this as a typical posture when driving, ironing or sitting at an office desk. Now alternate the two movements, squirming like a belly dancer. Repeat several times and let go.

Bring your attention to your stomach. Pull it in as far as you can and hold it until you can identify the effect of this action throughout your body. As you do so ask yourself what you may be holding in, and then let go. Repeat three times, and then allow your stomach and back to flop. Take a few moments to experience this sensation and allow it to spread throughout your lower body.

When you have done this, bring your attention to your chest. Notice your heartbeat. Is it quiet and regular, or loud and irregular; pounding, or racing? Pay attention to your breathing. Is it shallow, deep, regular, irregular, difficult, easy? How does it compare with your heartbeat in this respect?

Now imagine that tattooed on your chest you have a large, exotic butterfly emerging from a cocoon. Breathe in deeply, and as you do so imagine the butterfly spreading its wings to their full extent. At the point where the butterfly seems about to fly off, breathe out and watch how this affects it. Repeat this five times.

Still paying attention to your breathing, raise your shoulders and observe the effect on the butterfly. Then drop them, observing their effect. Push your shoulders back and observe the effect on the butterfly. Then, doing likewise, draw your shoulders forward.

Now bring your attention to your shoulders. Raise them to your ears and hold them in that position, noting their effects on the upper part of your body, before letting them drop. Repeat three times. Raise each shoulder independently, and as you hold the movement ask yourself whether you have ever been described as having a chip on your shoulder. If so, which shoulder seems to be the likely candidate? Rotate each shoulder through 360 degrees, and then both shoulders together, observing the effect on the shoulders, chest, back and elsewhere.

Having done this bring your attention down your right arm to your hand. Imagine that you are holding in that hand an ancient gold coin, the only one of its kind in existence, and therefore priceless. Grip it so tightly that there is no danger whatever of it slipping from your hand, and as you do so observe the effects of

15

this action not only in your hand, lower arm, upper arm and shoulder, but also on your neck, head, jaw and elsewhere in your body. Follow the effects of the action as far as they extend, and having reached the furthest point of influence, ask yourself what in life you are holding on to; what you have a firm grip on. Then when the action is becoming too painful to sustain further, carefully transfer the coin to your left hand, once again gripping it so there is no danger of it being lost. Tighten the grip and, as you follow the effect to its furthest extremity, ask yourself which hand has the stronger grip. Then ask yourself whether you hold onto different things with this side of yourself than the other, and what they are.

When you have answered the questions, toss the coin from the left hand to the right and then throw it away, allowing the fingers of both hands to fall loosely as you do so and your arms to fall by your sides. Ask yourself what you have let go of in life, and what you need to let go of.

Now imagine that the floor beneath you is beginning to rise. Resist this as forcefully as you can, spreading your fingers and the palms of your hands flat and pushing downwards. The floor continues to rise, forcing your hands upwards and obliging you to flex your arms against it. If the floor continues to rise you will be sandwiched against the ceiling, so press downwards with all your strength. Despite this the floor continues to rise, until, just as it seems you cannot resist further, the floor falls away, and your hands and arms with it. Allow your arms to flop at your side and take a few seconds to experience this sensation and allow it to spread.

Having done so bring your attention to your neck. Shift your head 180 degrees to the right, holding this position for a few seconds; then 180 degrees to the left, doing likewise. Then rotate your head through 360 degrees, taking note of aches, pains, and any other sensations. Be aware of the sheer weight of your head and the effort involved in keeping it upright. Then let it flop forward.

Bring your attention up the back of your neck and across your scalp. Try to wiggle your scalp, and your ears if you can.

Raise your eyebrows and hold the action, observing the effects on the rest of your head and face. Then drop your brows. Now pull your brows down towards your chin, and hold the action. Which of these movements is more typical of you? Feel the effects of this movement on your head and neck. Now let go.

Bringing your attention to your nose, flare the nostrils as widely as possible. Do things 'get up your nose'? Tighten your nostrils, and as you do so, ask yourself whether you tend to sniff at things. Stretch your upper lip downwards, and hold this action. Perhaps you try to keep a stiff upper lip?

Press your lips tightly together. As you hold this action notice its effects on the remainder of your face, and ask yourself whether you are tight-lipped about anything.

Now clench your teeth as tightly as possible. Do you feel you grit your teeth against life? Or do you tend to bite off more than you can chew? Do you bite back what you want to say, or snap at people? Notice the effects of this action on the muscles of your face, head, neck and chest. Do you tend to suffer pain in any of these areas?

Now shift your jaw from side to side. Many migraine sufferers tend to do this without being aware of it. Notice the effects on the temples and elsewhere. Ask yourself if life is a grind.

Let your mouth hang open. It is impossible to be fully relaxed while the mouth is shut as it is necessary to tighten the jaw muscles to effect this. How do you feel when open-mouthed?

Now breathe in through your nose and out through your open mouth, observing how this feels and its effects on the body. Continue to breathe in this way for a few moments. Then bring your attention back to your feet. Scan your body upwards noting any tightness, discomfort or pain in any region, and relax it by alternately tightening and then letting go of the muscles there. If the tightness, discomfort or pain persists, make a mental note of it. This is significant because it needs to be dealt with before full relaxation can be achieved.

To the count of 1 – let go of the muscles of your feet and legs; 2 – let go of the muscles of your lower back and stomach; 3 – let go of the muscles of your arms, shoulders and chest; 4 – let go of your head; 5 – let go of the muscles of your jaw.

Spend a few moments becoming aware of the sensations throughout your body. If relaxed, your limbs should feel heavy and warm. These are the physiological effects produced by relaxation of muscle fibres and the vasolidation of blood vessels.

Now imagine yourself in a pleasant situation where you feel relaxed, at ease, comfortable and secure. Notice whether you are alone, with other people or animals, and whether these are known to you or not. Pay attention to the sights, sounds and smells of this place; how it feels, and how you feel in it. Notice all the details of the scene as vividly as possible and allow yourself to enjoy being there.

Spend some time exploring the situation and becoming fully

acquainted with it. Having done so, ask yourself the following questions:

- How easy or otherwise do you find this imaginary exercise?
- Are your images or impressions primarily visual? If not, what kinds of images are they, and how vividly do you sense them?
- What aspects of this imaginary situation do you find particularly restful or relaxing?
- What features of your everyday life are you getting away from in this situation? If it isn't clear to you, compare the imaginary situation with the usual situations of your everyday life.
- What might this imaginary exercise tell you about the stressors in your life?

When you have answered these questions remember that this imaginary place is always there for you to go to. You carry it around inside yourself and can go there any time you wish.

Prepare to open your eyes and return your awareness to your surroundings. Now do so, and take a few moments to orientate yourself before recording the significant features of the exercise, including your answers to the previous questions.

Commentary

Many people, especially those who claim to find it difficult to relax or go to sleep, are astonished to find themselves relaxed, sometimes to the extent of 'drifting off' or falling asleep (and snoring), even in the most unlikely circumstances. It is perhaps worth noting in this connection that I have successfully induced relaxation in an unsoundproofed glass building adjacent to the central bus depot and fire station of a busy town on market day, with bell-ringing practice taking place in a nearby church (it is quite remarkable how frequently the fire brigade can be summoned on a wet winter day!); and in a room over a dance studio where an enthusiastic aerobics group was working out to rock and pop music and quite literally raising the roof.

Some people 'come to' or awake puzzled, and quite oblivious of the instructions given in the later stages of the exercise. Often these individuals are sure they were not asleep but have little or no recollection of parts of the exercise, or of potential distractions such as fire-bells or police sirens. Some people describe experiencing a pleasant 'woozy' feeling or a 'drifting' in and out of ordinary conscious awareness. Some describe a fuzziness or dizziness, while others are alarmed by sudden jerks which are normally experienced by people as they are falling asleep.

Most people find the experience very pleasant and are reluctant to draw it to a conclusion. When they do they are usually surprised that the exercise has taken the time it has, reporting that time appears to have 'flown'. Indeed one of the major features of relaxation is that it modifies our sense of time, which, as we shall see, has considerable implications for healing, and especially for pain control. People commonly report having experienced sensations of warmth and heaviness throughout their body, a 'glow' of contentment. They may experience other bodily sensations such as vibrations, waves, feelings of being suspended or very light. Feelings of calmness, tranquillity and detachment are also commonly reported. Others report tingling or 'pins and needles' in limbs or body parts, loss of sensation, and feelings of the arms being 'on the wrong way round', or the hands on different arms.

These sensations are sometimes alarming or experienced as unpleasant, but they are entirely consistent with the physiological shifts that occur during progressive relaxation, and are a clear indication that the individual is achieving the desired state.

Some people find that as they relax they encounter a residual anxiety, often quite unspecific, but sufficiently disturbing to prevent them progressing or sustaining the level of relaxation already achieved. Sometimes the source of the anxiety will be quite specific, as is the case with those persons who cannot imagine a place in which they would feel secure.

Intrusive and unpleasant imagery may arise which generates anxiety and tension and prevents relaxation. These features need to be addressed, not simply because they prevent the person relaxing fully, but because they may reveal the unconscious fears, anxieties, concerns or memories of the person, which produce tension and may contribute to stress-related conditions.

Some people experience a spontaneous release of emotion as certain muscles relax. One woman burst into tears when letting go her grip on the imaginary gold coin and recognised in this her fears of letting go of her children, the most valuable feature of her life. On relaxing her mouth another woman cried out in horror at the memory of seeing her mother like this on her deathbed, and realised as she did so that her current tensions related to her unexpressed grief.

This feature of relaxation highlights the fundamental principle of what might be termed psychosomatic medicine, which is the recognition that there is no separation between mind and body, and that we react as a whole organism to the events and experiences of our lives. This understanding owes much to the insights of the psychotherapist Wilhelm Reich, who observed that people respond to mental events physically as well as mentally. Reich proposed that the psychological defence mechanisms indicated by his early mentor Sigmund Freud are matched by physical defences, or 'armouring', intended to provide protection against further attack or trauma. These postures and physical expressions become habitual over time and characteristic of the in-dividual. According to Reich, these character patterns, as he termed them, give important clues to the psychological and emotional state of the person. However, they often produce physical stresses and distortions, and even illness. Unlike Freud, therefore, who was concerned exclusively with mental defences and thus with psychoanalysis, Reich was concerned with 'character analysis' of the whole person. This involved noting areas of muscular tension and distortion in the body and working on them directly through physical manipulation to restore them to normal position and functioning. He found that this frequently gives rise to spontaneous emotional release, or catharsis, which is often very powerful; and to spontaneous remembering of the original situation which prompted the initial defence. Relaxation of muscles may therefore result in sudden and unexpected emotional out-bursts.

Generally, however, people have pleasant imagery and little difficulty in generating it, although they may find it very puzzling. Some, finding their imagination 'playing odd tricks', that is, producing unexpected imagery or that which they regard as unacceptable to themselves or others, may attempt to censor or change it. For example, an attractive woman imagined herself in bed with a partner, and although she found this most pleasurable and relaxing, thought she shouldn't and so imagined herself at a rather dull seaside resort. She was still with the same partner but in a considerably less intimate and enjoyable situation.

This kind of censorship is potentially very significant because the 'shoulds' and 'should nots' that dominate people's lives often generate stress and illness. All too frequently one encounters women who cannot allow themselves to relax because they feel that they 'should' be looking after others and 'should not' be indulging themselves; and men who feel that they 'must' work around the clock to support others and 'must not' take time off for themselves. Even if they give themselves permission to relax, these self-imposed imperatives prevent them doing so effectively. For example, one woman attempting progressive relaxation reported imagining herself sitting in a beautiful pine forest thoroughly enjoying its delicious scent until she began to 'smell' burning toast. This reminded her that she 'should' be at home carrying out domestic chores rather than taking it easy, and she immediately returned to normal consciousness with a start.

For those people who believe there are specific ways in which things should or should not be done, concern about whether they are doing the exercise 'properly' may be sufficient to inhibit relaxation or the production of imagery, because their anxiety translates into muscular tension. This not only highlights the importance of relaxation in facilitating imagery but also illustrates the way in which concern about performance, achievement, success, failure or evaluation creates tensions in people's lives and limits their experience. One woman indicated that it was only through attempting progressive relaxation that she became aware how anxious she was not to fail in anything she did. Others who successfully relax and produce imagery often express concern that they might not be doing so correctly because they see themselves in the scene in a detached manner, as though looking down on themselves. This in no way reduces the potency or validity of the imagery. However, many people have a very real difficulty in recognising what constitutes imagery, or acknowledging their imagery as the product of their imagination.

Many people believe that unless their images are wholly invented they are not truly imaginary. This often reflects a considerable confusion between fantasy and reality. Some insist that, because a scene they visualise has a real-life counterpart, their imagery is a product of memory rather than the imagination. Such a view implies that inner representations of the outer world are 'real' in some sense, which is not the case. Many of those who fail to make this distinction regard 'reality' as an immutable, objective domain outside of themselves, in some way fixed and beyond their control. They fail to recognise the extent to which they create that reality through their beliefs, assumptions, expectations and imaginings, and thus the degree of choice they have in determining their lives. For such people the idea that you can create a different reality by cultivating a different outlook or attitude towards it, or by seeing it in a different light, is often very difficult to grasp. They therefore tend to see the events and circumstances of their lives as fixed and their responses to them as unavoidable. Accordingly stress is often seen as an inevitability rather than a choice, which, as we shall see, has important implications for health.

Furthermore those who fail to recognise that their imagery is not 'real' may also not readily appreciate that other 'realities' of their existence, such as their fears and anxieties, their expectations and assumptions, their self-image and identity, may also be wholly or in part imaginary, and a source of unnecessary and avoidable stress.

The specific imagery conjured by individuals is greatly variable. Some people imagine themselves on beaches, or in the sea, often at favourite holiday resorts, in the mountains or other areas of natural beauty, or in more commonplace outdoor settings such as gardens, allotments, parks, canal sides and riverbanks. Others visualise themselves indoors, in comfortable chairs, a warm bath or bed, cuddling animals or children (more usually the former, which may say something about the British), watching fish or birds, or engaging in a favourite pastime. This highlights the often-overlooked therapeutic significance of leisure activities and pastimes, the natural environment and animals.

Recognition of the latter, in particular, is often obscured in mass-media scares about the health menace presented by pets. However, there is extensive evidence that companion animals can have a very positive effect on the health and well-being of humans. Studies have shown that interactions with pets have a favourable influence on the physiology of the heart and circulatory function, because stroking a cat or dog reduces heart rate and blood pressure (Ahmedazi, 1987). Animals may also be positively therapeutic for the elderly and those who are bereaved, depressed or living alone, by alleviating loneliness and isolation, giving and receiving affection, and encouraging physical activity. Increasing interest in the advantages to the sick and elderly of having contact with pets has led to various schemes where dogs and other pets are taken into hospitals, hospices, homes for the elderly, children's homes, hospital wards and prisons (Scarlett, 1987; Whyte, 1987). Where such schemes have been implemented, staff have also been observed to derive increased job satisfaction and be less stressed, largely as a result of seeing those in their care more alert and happy. Thus, although many people have yet to be persuaded of the health benefits of pet animals, they are increasingly being introduced into health-care settings to provide company and comfort for residents; and patients recovering from illness, especially heart conditions, are encouraged to spend time stroking their pets.

Questions

In the foregoing exercise the relaxation procedure is augmented at various points by imagery and I am often asked whether this is to facilitate relaxation or whether it serves some other function. The answer is 'yes' on both counts. Imagery is known to enhance relaxation because it is generally absorbing, and when thus engrossed there is a tendency to 'let go' of or suspend the usual concerns, conflicts, preoccupations and anxieties that give rise to tensions. Time, which in itself is often a source of stress, passes unobserved and quickly.

The specific images employed are chosen because they reinforce the actions suggested. So, for example, the butterfly image augments the expansion of the chest and helps establish a pattern of breathing that assists relaxation.

However, the butterfly is also a potent symbol. The Greek word *psyche* means both butterfly and soul, and universally the butterfly represents spiritual qualities, transformation, metamorphosis, change and freedom. The way a person construes this image may therefore be significant at a number of levels. One woman who raised the question of the possible significance of the images employed was concerned by the fact that she had difficulty expanding the butterfly on her chest on the 'in' breath. She felt that her chest was like a balloon which she could only inflate when exhaling. It was suggested to her that she may generally find it easier to be outwardly expansive in the sense of giving out or putting out herself, rather than inwardly expansive. This she felt to be very true of her and to give rise to various stresses and problems in her life.

On a purely physical level, however, her difficulty highlights the fact that many people breathe improperly, using very little lung space, and find it easier to breathe out than to draw breath in. Another woman in the same group was concerned by the fact that although she could visualise her butterfly vividly, seeing it emerging exotic and colourful from its cocoon and spreading its wings expansively, she could do this only once, as she regarded it as impossible to put it back in the cocoon. She therefore held her breath to avoid the butterfly shrinking, which enhanced rather than reduced her tension. This reveals two features, the first being her conscious, rational control over the imagery. Her logic told her that the butterfly would not go back into its cocoon. This conscious, rational control of imagery and the application of logic to it is a common problem for those who fear loss of control, and, as in this case, it tends to inhibit the generation of imagery and any benefits to be derived from it. On a different level, her emotional reaction to the butterfly suggests that unconsciously it held particular symbolic significance for her. Indeed, she subsequently acknowledged

24

that both the tendency to conscious control and rational thought, and a desire to be free forever of the restrictions of her life, including the former, were characteristic of her.

Another commonly asked question is how often should a person relax, and when is it best to do so?

It is generally recommended that a person sets aside two 20-minute periods a day in which to relax. However, it depends on the purpose of relaxation. If being employed as part of the treatment for a specific condition, more frequent or longer periods may be beneficial, whereas if relaxation is being used for the development of self-awareness fewer periods may be appropriate. In the final analysis, the individual should determine what appears most beneficial to them, and should build this into their daily routine. For most people this is the stumbling block. They appreciate the benefits of relaxation but will not discipline themselves to set aside time each day for this purpose. Many will not take sufficient time to train themselves adequately in the relevant procedures, and will tend to rely on external aids, claiming that they are unable to relax themselves. This is why many people prefer to join a relaxation class. However, while this may be a pleasurable occasion it is unlikely that it will confer many benefits if it is the sole period of relaxation in a week. As to suitable times of day for relaxation, morning and evening are frequently recommended, or before meals. Again, the most appropriate time is that which suits the individual and his or her lifestyle. Many people find that relaxation is beneficial before sleep.

This raises the question of whether sleep is 'better' than relaxation.

The answer would appear to be 'no'. Research suggests that short periods of relaxation may yield shifts in physiological functioning which are achieved only after several hours of sleep, and that relaxation is more refreshing than sleep.

Many people then ask whether it is 'bad' to fall asleep while relaxing.

Given the above, sleep may not be as physically beneficial as relaxation. From the psychological point of view, falling asleep prevents the development of awareness and insight into oneself that might otherwise have been achieved (unless of course the person keeps a record of their dream imagery and uses it for this purpose). Those whose primary interest is in self-awareness are advised to adopt sitting postures in which sleep is less likely to occur. However, if insomnia is a problem for the individual, then falling asleep will be welcomed and is likely to be beneficial.

A question always asked is whether audiotapes are useful aids to relaxation.

The ultimate aim of all forms of relaxation training is to teach the individual self-reliance and self-awareness. For this reason dependence *solely* on external aids is not to be encouraged. Nevertheless, audiotapes are a valuable aid to relaxation, especially for beginners, and are justifiably very popular. They are most useful in helping people to memorise a procedure, especially where this is lengthy and/or complex, and are recommended for such a purpose in the preface to this book. Perhaps even more importantly, they enable people to designate a particular period of time for relaxation, a habit which, once developed, facilitates awareness and use of internal cues to relaxation. They thus introduce discipline into the process of relaxation.

Audiotapes can also be played while we are engaged in other activities, enabling us to cultivate awareness of the tensions involved in those tasks. They have many applications in various therapeutic contexts, and are widely used and prescribed by healing practitioners. When used with a personal stereo they are infinitely adaptable. Not only are they easily carried and employed, but they have the additional advantage of screening out all other sound stimuli and distractions. They can thus be used in various settings: on public transport and beaches; in the dentist's chair or doctor's waiting room; in hospitals and labour wards; before and during surgery (an application becoming more widespread); and before interviews, examinations, sporting events and public performances. This adaptability provides people who wish to train themselves in relaxation with increased opportunities to do so, and provides them with an ideal gift for those they believe would benefit from doing likewise.

However, care should be taken in the audiotapes chosen as aids to relaxation. Some give the misleading impression that progressive relaxation is easily and quickly achieved. Those who, upon using them, find that this is not the case can easily become discouraged, conclude that they cannot relax, and give up trying altogether. Such 'aids' are clearly counterproductive. A good relaxation tape should make it clear that relaxation is a progressive and learned process, a training in self-awareness and 'muscle sense' that requires practice and dedicated time.

Progressive relaxation is a lengthy procedure but there are quicker ways of achieving relaxation. A shorter, simpler approach to relaxation is examined in the following chapter.

2

MAKING TIME FOR HEALTH AND HEALING

We haven't the time to take our time.
Eugene Ionesco

One of the most commonly reported effects of relaxation is a change in the perception of time. Most people considerably underestimate the duration of relaxation periods, experiencing them as brief, irrespective of the amount of 'clocktime' they occupy, and for many the sense of time is suspended completely.

This feature is not only characteristic of all relaxation procedures but of any activity in which we become absorbed. When thus engrossed time seems to 'fly' or is lost track of, hence these activities are appropriately termed 'pastimes'. Frequently they are dismissed as trivial or insignificant features of our lives, but this view has to be reappraised in the light of evidence which suggests that a person's relationship to time is a central factor in the promotion of health and illness.

The experience of time

Broadly speaking, people experience time in one of two ways: as being on their side, or against them; that is, as friend or foe. Those who are 'time friendly' are typically more leisurely and unhurried in their approach to life, working at their own pace. They are generally well-organised and efficient, setting realistic goals and deadlines. As a result they tend to meet schedules and keep appointments. They are able to take time with other people, whether family, friends or work colleagues, and to make time for their interests, leisure activities and holidays, and to enjoy themselves.

The lifestyle of those who are 'time conflicted' is very different. They possess a sense of urgency, usually attempting to do too much too quickly, and expecting immediate results. Their objectives and schedules are unrealistic, and consequently they never have enough time. They are constantly rushing to meet deadlines and keep appointments, and are often late for both; or they make excessive demands on themselves, working day and night to achieve their aims. They tend to hurry and panic, to leave tasks unfinished, to give insufficient attention to them, or to put them off until later. As a result they tend to create a backlog of undone or uncompleted tasks, and so either cannot make time for leisure activities and holidays, or feel guilty if they do.

Although often inefficient themselves, they tend to be impatient with others, whom they expect to respond immediately to their requests and demands. A common word in their vocabulary is 'just' – as in 'I "just" need this', or ' "just" do that', 'I'll do it "just" now', or 'in "just" a minute'. These people typically take little time to consider the needs or wishes of others. Not surprisingly, therefore, they tend to create pressures for, and tensions in, those around them.

A good example is the man who reported that when home decorating he sets himself the task of completing each room 'in just one go', working through the night until the following morning in order to meet his self-imposed deadline, and obliging his wife to forego her sleep to fetch and carry for him and make innumerable snacks and pots of tea. It is not surprising, therefore, that the work standards of time-conflicted people tend to suffer, often creating further problems for them. Such people are constantly under pressure and stressed by time.

Time stress

The word *stress* is thought to derive from the Latin *stringere*, meaning to draw tight or tighten, which aptly describes its effects on the body. The stressed individual is drawn tight mentally and physically, and feels 'strung out' or 'uptight'. These tensions, when sustained, impose strain on the organs and functions of the body, predisposing it to illness, and the individual to premature death.

Evidence that the time-stressed person is living dangerously comes from extensive research (Friedman and Rosenham, 1974), which was instigated by the chance remark of an upholsterer repairing the armchairs in the day-room of the heart unit in a US hospital. He noted that only the front edges of the chairs were worn, as though the occupants had been sitting on the edge of their seats in tense expectation. This matched the experience of two heart specialists who had observed that their patients tended to have a continual sense of time urgency, and an inability to sit back and relax. On the basis of subsequent research they developed a detailed profile of two personality types, which they rather unimaginatively distinguished as A and B. These were found to be relatively stable traits throughout the lifespan and identifiable in young children, students and adults.

Comparisons between them proved clear-cut and startling. Type A individuals, who broadly conform to what are here referred to as time-conflicted persons, were found to be 'engaged in a relatively chronic and excessive struggle to obtain a usually unlimited number of things from their environment in the shortest period of time, or against the opposing efforts of other persons or things in that environment'. This striving translates into physical behaviours such as brisk movements, fist clenching during normal conversation, explosive and hurried speech, rapid eating, upper chest breathing, tension, easily aroused hostility and fierce impatience. The concomitant physiological effects are high blood pressure, elevation of blood hormones such as adrenalin, insulin and hydrocortisone, which are normally raised only during periods of urgency or stress, increased respiratory rate, sweat-gland activity and muscle tension. Furthermore 28 per cent of Type A individuals were found to exhibit clear signs of coronary heart disease, compared with only 4 per cent of Type B persons, and to be significantly more likely to succumb to hypertension, migraine, ulcers and gastrointestinal disorders, stroke and kidney disease – disorders which collectively have been described as 'time' or 'hurry sickness'. Indeed Type A persons are more likely to develop stress-related conditions, that is, most illnesses, as stress is now acknowledged to be a major factor in high blood pressure, chronic backache, arthritis, allergies, vertigo, multiple sclerosis, diabetes, skin conditions, constipation and menstrual difficulties, and a significant factor in smoking, overeating, alcohol and drug abuse. It has also been found to suppress the functions of the immune system, and to be implicated in the development of certain cancers.

Type A persons have also been found to be significantly more likely to die suddenly, and at a relatively early age, thereby confirming the wisdom of the matchbox caption which suggests that 'sudden death is Nature's way of telling us to slow down'.

Although these behaviour patterns are relatively stable characteristics of an individual, they may nevertheless undergo change. The most 'laid-back' Type B person may occasionally show Type A features, and may sustain them if he becomes caught up in the treadmill of modern life. Unfortunately, contemporary Western culture encourages the Type A lifestyle, which is presented within the media as a model to which everyone should aspire. Many who do so, induced by the prospect of high salaries and prestige, recognise and accept the high risk of 'burn out' in early middle age or even sooner, and anticipate a more leisurely lifestyle following a mid-life career change or early retirement, oblivious of the fact that they might not be alive or well enough to enjoy it.

The likelihood of this happening can be significantly reduced by participation in various activities, such as relaxation, which help to modify time perception and to promote a better relationship with time, but Type A persons are unlikely to make time for them, that is, unless or until illness obliges them to rethink their lives (see Hughes and Molloy, 1990).

Ironically, people making career changes or retiring from work altogether are often given a clock as a leaving present!

For the less fortunate, time simply runs out.

31

Time and disease

Time may be a significant factor in determining the course of disease in those who have succumbed to it. When people become ill their perception of time may alter, and the more serious the illness the greater this is likely to be. Worry that one's 'time is up' generates stress, which does nothing to help the problem, and may have an adverse effect.

It has been found that those who are intensely anxious following an acute heart attack are less likely to survive than those who remain calm. This is because the anxiety of the former translates into high blood pressure and increased secretion of adrenalin, which may cause rapid and chaotic heart beat and result in sudden death. The increase in heart rate and blood pressure requires the heart to do more work and necessitates more oxgyen, which cannot be supplied because oxygen lack resulting from obstruction of one of the coronary arteries which supply the heart with blood caused the heart attack in the first place. Therefore more attacks are likely.

Time-related anxiety can thus kill, and it can hasten death in terminal illness. Even if it does not, it will almost certainly ensure that the person derives little enjoyment from what time they do have.

Time and death

The question 'How much time have I got?' is usually the first one asked following diagnosis of serious illness, and the doctor's prognosis all too frequently becomes a self-fulfilling prophecy because the resulting panic, anxiety and depression are in themselves malignant. Recognition of the fact that many people effectively destroy themselves in response to the expectations of others that their 'time is up' has led to widespread condemnation of the medical practice of specifying a patient's life expectancy. However, in Western culture there is generally held to be a 'normal' life expectancy of 'threescore years and ten', and so time-related anxiety is a feature of ageing in some quite healthy people who believe their time is 'running out'.

Time and pain

Time may also affect the experience of pain, which is often a feature of chronic illness and is generally experienced as unpleasant. The content of time intervals is known to be a major determinant of how they are experienced. Most people recognise that when they are engaged in an unpleasant or uninteresting activity time 'drags' or constricts, whereas when they are engaged in an interesting or pleasurable activity it 'flies' or expands. Evidence suggests that pain can be lessened by stretching the sense of time. In effect this is what analgesic or pain-killing drugs do – they expand the sense of time in much the same way that relaxation does. However, any activity which 'kills time' can have pain-killing effects. Therefore the person who is time friendly and takes time for their interests and pastimes is less likely to experience pain than the person who never has time to do so.

Time and energy

Another feature which distinguishes time-friendly and time-conflicted persons is that the latter typically appear to lack energy, and so, despite their efforts and their urgency, they frequently achieve considerably less than those who are time friendly. It may be observed that those people who have plenty of time also appear to have abundant energy, while those who have no energy tend to have no time. Thus it seems that those who use their time effectively tend to use their energies effectively, and vice versa. This time energy equation has important implications for health, as is evident even on the most superficial scrutiny. Sleep is energising and refreshing, as are all forms of relaxation, the effects of which have been likened to 'recharging one's batteries'. Conversely, healing approaches such as T'ai Chi, yoga, acupuncture, acupressure, reflexology, bioenergetic therapies, therapeutic touch and the laying on of hands, which work directly to promote energy flow within the body, promote relaxation.

However, despite the fact that 'lack of energy' is one of the most common presenting symptoms in medical practice, orthodox medicine generally fails to recognise, much less understand, the relationship between time and energy.

The treatments most likely to be prescribed by the physician are medications, vitamins or rest, and while the latter is appropriate, it is not easily achieved by most people, especially those who experience difficulties in relation to time.

The person is rarely, if ever, asked to consider why they lack energy, what they are doing to deplete it, or how they could use their energies more effectively. Even if asked, most people would be unable to provide an answer, because despite commonly describing themselves and others in energy images, few people give much thought to what they actually mean. This difficulty is not confined to the ordinary man or woman in the street, but also pervades the scientific community because, although the concept of energy is fundamental to physics, that branch of knowledge which attempts to explain the physical universe and is thus the basis of all other sciences, its definition remains somewhat vague and imprecise.

Time and energy: the traditional view

In the tradition of physics established by Isaac Newton in the seventeenth century, energy is viewed as 'work', and although its relevance may not be immediately apparent, this nevertheless has important implications for health and illness.

It takes 'work' to tighten muscles and to sustain this tension. Lying in bed with tense muscles may actually involve more work, and be a greater drain on one's energy, than digging the garden or wielding a pick-axe, because in the latter, after an initial impetus, effort is reduced through the principle of inertia. Paradoxically, therefore, work may involve less 'work' than rest, and when a person maintains muscular tension over time, the work involved may be considerable, draining energy resources, progressively tiring him, and imposing strain on the body. Without respite, he will become 'worn out' doing nothing. Someone who is constantly time-pressured remains tense, and therefore expends energy without realising it. Thus, as Jacobsen (1977)

observes, hurry sicknesses or stress disorders are manifesta-
tions of energy extravagance, because tense, time-stressed
people expend too much energy and therefore excessive
adenosine triphosphate or cyclic TCP, the basic chemical
used in nerve and muscle cells. People with chronic tension
often become locked into a self-perpetuating cycle where,
although tired, their muscular tensions prevent them relaxing
or sleeping, further exhausting them, so that energy action
requires more and more effort or energy. They have neither
time nor energy.

Relaxation – which can be thought of as a 'letting go' of
tension – is necessary if this cycle is to be broken.

Time and energy: the modern view

According to the new vision of reality afforded by physics
during this century, the entire universe *is* energy, and can be
understood as dynamic patterns of change or movement.
Every phenomenon within the universe is thus energy in a
certain state of vibration (from the Latin *vibrare*, to move).
Accordingly colour, sound and light are merely different
forms of energy, as are thoughts, emotions and images, and
all material forms. Matter, or mass, and energy are simply
different aspects of the same phenomenon. It is this relationship, expressed in Einstein's famous equation $E=mc^2$ (where
E = energy, m = mass and c = the speed of light), which
forms the basis of Relativity Theory and Quantum Physics.
Mass is thus no longer associated with any material
substance or 'stuff', but with bundles or 'quanta' of energy,
or activity, and necessarily therefore must be understood in
relation to time. It follows from this that time and energy are
reciprocal, and that any change in one will necessarily effect
a change in the other. Modifications of the perception of time
therefore have implications for energy and vice versa. Release
of energy thus not only involves 'letting go' of the muscle
tension in which it is bound up, but also a 'letting go' or
relaxation of the normal time sense.

Indeed, focus solely on physical relaxation tends to obscure
the fact that bodily tensions are generated in response to
mental and emotional tensions, such as conflicts, fears and

anxieties. If these psychological tensions are not relaxed then it follows that physical relaxation will prove difficult and, at best, will be limited.

MEDITATION

Research has shown that complete physical relaxation is possible only when all mental processes are suspended, and the mind is blank (Jacobsen, 1938). This is the desired end of all forms of meditation, and is variously described as nirvana, satori, no-mind, void, or cosmic consciousness. Its attainment involves the gradual relinquishing of mental attitudes, preoccupations and concerns, and is therefore not simply the development of bodily awareness but awareness of the self at all levels. Meditation is thus a complete letting go or abandonment of all notions about the self and the world, all beliefs and ideals, assumptions and interpretations. It is a state of no mind, no will and no action, which is often described as a state of pure being, and claimed as the ultimate in relaxation and therefore as medicine.

Support for these claims comes from a wealth of research (see Graham, 1990), much of which has employed subtle physiological measurements by sophisticated recording devices. It is now clear that meditation confers a variety of beneficial effects. These include changes in the electrical activity of the brain, slowing of respiratory and heart rate, and lowering of blood pressure, all of which are suggestive of a state of deep relaxation. Other measures confirm that meditation is a highly relaxed but wakeful state and that it generates an integrated physiological response which is the opposite to that generated by stress. Various psychological effects consistent with this state have also been found, including greater stability of mood, lower anxiety and a greater sense of being effective in the world.

Awareness of the therapeutic possibilities of meditation has led to its application in the treatment of stress and stress-related conditions. It has been used successfully in the treatment of asthma, phobias and hypertension, where it is found to be more effective than drugs. The volume of evidence leaves little doubt that meditation is an effective antidote to anxiety, and also suggests that it may confer long-term health benefits, promoting a habitual low arousal state and reducing the intake of alcohol, cigarettes, coffee, meat and sugar. Increasingly, therefore, meditation is being recommended within orthodox medicine for the prevention and treatment of disease.

Transcendental Meditation

The most extensively researched form of meditation is Transcendental Meditation, or TM, which is based on a traditional Hindu practice. It has been promoted in the West by Maharishi Mahesh Yogi and is supported by a vast international organisation, the International Meditation Society, which claims to have several million members worldwide. For this reason, and because its procedures are simple and well standardised, large-scale studies under well-controlled conditions have been possible. TM has been studied in a whole range of applications, and there is little doubt as to its effectiveness. What is more doubtful is the claim made by its proponents that TM is unique in producing these effects. Research suggests that meditation is little different in this regard from other forms of relaxation (West, 1979, 1980). Moreover, the claims of the International Meditation Society that TM does not involve any kind of philosophical belief, religious commitment or group membership are questionable, given that the TM organisation acts to recruit members with the aim of establishing an 'enlightened' international community with quite specific objectives. This makes it unattractive to many who might derive benefit from it. Furthermore, because the induction procedure and details of practice of TM are kept secret, and relevant research findings can only be published with the permission of the International Meditation Society, it is not acceptable to clinical practice and research, the conventions of which dictate that procedures and findings are made available for public scrutiny and testing.

The Relaxation Response

There have been various attempts to strip the basic TM technique of its more esoteric trappings. The most successful, whose effectiveness has been demonstrated by research, is that developed by Herbert Benson, a pioneer of research into TM, heart specialist and professor at Harvard Medical School.

Benson claims that it is not necessary to meditate, be wired up to complex machinery or engage in esoteric rites and practices in order to achieve relaxation, because it is not a learned phenomenon or skill but a universal human capacity which requires no special aptitude, specific method of induction or lengthy period of training, only practice and time dedicated to it.

Benson has developed a simple procedure for eliciting this 'relaxation response', which focuses primarily on improving the efficiency of breathing, but also involves visual imagery. Breathing is important because it provides the oxygen necessary to release energy from food and deliver it to the muscles. Increase in oxygen intake therefore makes more energy available. Many people, notably those who are Type A, breath rapidly using only their upper chest and so do not take in sufficient oxygen. By focusing attention on breathing, Benson's method diverts the mind from its normal preoccupations, enabling relaxation to occur progressively as mental tensions are relinquished. Relaxation is enhanced further by encouraging the individual to imagine a pleasant scene. The introduction of mental imagery facilitates absorption in what might be thought of as the 'picture shows' of the mind, which helps to modify the time sense, and also introduces flexibility in other mental functions through the creation of new experiences and perspectives.

Relaxation of mental habits

Flexibility of mental functioning is recognised as an important determinant of an individual's effectiveness, his capacity for psychological and social adjustment and, ultimately, his survival; and increasingly its implications for health and illness are being acknowledged. Studies of those who survive, whether war and its consequences, or serious illness, have shown that their characteristic traits are biphasic, that is, they are both serious *and* playful, logical *and* intuitive, rational *and* emotional, hardworking *and* lazy, introspective *and* outgoing, and so on, rather than one or the other (Siegel, 1990). As a result they do not fit neatly into any of the normal psychological categories, and are considerably more flexible and adaptable than most people, with a wider array of resources to draw upon. Similarly, studies have shown that individuals who manifest both masculine and feminine traits are significantly more healthy, both physically and psychologically, than those who conform to the stereotypical traits of one or other gender.

Flexibility is also known to be a particularly crucial factor in recovery from illness, those who respond poorly to treatment usually being characterised by inflexibility or an unwillingness to make changes. This inflexibility or rigidity is known to be a feature of a number of medical conditions, including cancers, rheumatoid arthritis, coronary heart disease and other stress-related disorders, and of poor psychological adjustment, especially in old age. Certainly, by limiting the individual's perspectives and experiences to what is familiar and known, mental rigidity restricts the way in which they deal with the ordinary issues of their lives, and especially their problems.

Several factors tend to limit flexibility, and hence the possibilities for coping in a given situation. These include the mental habits acquired over the years which result in people becoming set in their ways and rigid in attitude and outlook and also negative thoughts, beliefs and expectations which greatly reduce the likelihood of new possibilities and solutions.

It is often said that as soon as a problem arises its solution is born, but the difficulty for most people is that in concentrating on certain features of the problem they fail to see the possibilities for solution. So, although they believe themselves to be looking for the solution they are actually hanging on to the problem.

Individuals vary greatly in the extent to which these factors

39

influence their thinking. Certain mental habits are encouraged within Western culture where, because of its emphasis
on language skills, there is a tendency to represent issues
verbally. This may be effective where these issues lend
themselves to verbal analysis, but many do not. Hence verbal
representation may not be particularly helpful in addressing
physical, emotional and psychological issues, which by their
nature are non-verbal.

Imagery provides an alternative means of representing
issues. It is a different way of looking at them, quite literally,
which may yield new and significant insights, different
possibilities, and enable problems to be transformed into
solutions. Additionally, by allowing issues to be approached
in a different way, it helps relax rigid mental attitudes,
beliefs, thoughts, expectations and habits which constrain
people in inappropriate, ineffective, outmoded and even
unhealthy coping strategies, and introduces flexibility into
their functioning.

The following exercise combines Benson's relaxation
method with imagery directed towards an assessment of the
energy status of the individual.

Exercise 2
'Energy' imagery facilitated by the Benson method of relaxation

Find somewhere quiet and make yourself comfortable, either sitting
or lying (preferably the former as the latter is likely to promote
sleep).

Close your eyes, or focus with open eyes on a fixed point or
object. Become aware of your breathing by inhaling through your
nose and exhaling through your mouth.

With each out-breath silently say 'One' and continue to repeat
this formula, breathing in and then out to the count of one. Don't
worry about achieving relaxation, simply allow this to occur at its
own pace.

Don't dwell on distracting thoughts, memories or concerns
which may arise, and do not try to suppress them. Merely make a
mental note of them and allow them to disappear. Then return your
attention to your breathing and the repetition of the word 'one',
and continue to do so for 10–20 minutes.

Having done this, scan your body for any residual tension. Should you encounter any, imagine it as ice. Note where it occurs and how it appears.

Now imagine that you are sitting or lying under a warm sun which, progressing from the head downwards, is melting the ice into a warm fluid which flows through your body and seeps out into the ground through the pores of your skin. Notice the nature of the fluid, its colour, density, clarity and movement, and also any areas that are resistant to the sun's warmth.

When the sun has melted all the physical tensions it can, allow its rays to dissolve any mental tensions you may have, letting them seep away, leaving your mind and body a clear channel without obstruction. Having done so, imagine yourself as an expanse of water. Note its location and any significant features of its surroundings, but pay particular attention to the colour, clarity, depth and quality of movement of the water itself.

When you are picturing it as vividly as you can, ask yourself the following questions:

- What might this image tell me about my energies and how effectively I am using them?
- What can I learn from it?

When you have answered these questions, bring your attention back to your breathing and gradually allow yourself to return to normal consciousness. Then make a verbal or written report of your experience, in the first-person present tense, noting the location and nature of your 'energy blocks', the manner in which they dissolved, and how easily or otherwise. Also note the details of the water imagery, paying particular attention to the features of colour, clarity, depth and movement, concluding with an assessment of what these features might indicate about your energies and how effectively you are using them.

Commentary

There are several reasons why it is desirable to describe imagery verbally in the first-person, present tense. One is that by so doing the verbal representational mode is re-engaged and can be brought to bear on the visually represented issues, thereby maximising mental flexibility and integrating verbal and non-verbal processes. This is important because effective functioning involves the whole person, rather than any

41

specific part or parts, and this synthesis, or wholeness, constitutes health. Furthermore, attaining balance between verbal and non-verbal processes is, as we shall see, essential to the maintenance of health.

The personalisation of imagery which results from its description in the first-person present tense is also important because many people have a tendency to deny responsibility for their own creations or products, whether their imaginings, thoughts, feelings, pains, actions or illnesses, attributing them to external rather than internal causes. This projection of personal features onto the outside world and others gives rise to the idea that these external forces are responsible for, or cause, them. Typically, therefore, people say 'He makes me angry' or 'It makes me sick', rather than 'I make myself angry or sick in response to' who or whatever it might be. Even more impersonal is the use of the word 'one', as in 'it amuses, or irritates, one'. Here a verbal ploy distances people from themselves as a source of their feelings, and from responsibility for them, by implying that their source is external and beyond personal control. The personalisation of images and feelings brought about by the use of the first-person and present tense works in reverse, helping to prompt acknowledgement of personal responsibility and locus of control: that is, the sense of being effective in the world rather than a passive victim of circumstance, and awareness of one's contribution to problems and illnesses.

This verbal shift also helps to highlight the possible significance of imagery. Frequently people will deny that there is any, arguing that the water they 'imagined' is 'real' – a stretch of the River Thames or Lake Geneva, their garden pond or local swimming baths. However, while it may correspond with a feature of the external world, it is nevertheless a product of their imagination, and its potential significance lies in why, of all the water they could have brought to mind or invented, they choose to imagine what they did. It isn't just any water, but a quite specific personal production or creation for which they are responsible, and which, for this very reason, is almost certainly meaningful when scrutinised more closely.

People who cannot readily see the personal relevance of an

image when viewed objectively may feel quite differently when they personalise it, or 'try it on'. Thus translated, 'a cool, unmoving pool with murky depths' becomes 'I am a cool, unmoving pool with murky depths', which, at the very least, gives food for thought. Put this way most people can see the significance of their imagery, and are shocked that a normally well-concealed aspect of themselves should have found expression in this way.

The majority of people see only too clearly *that* their images are significant, albeit not necessarily *what* their particular meaning may be. They therefore tend to look outside themselves for answers or solutions rather than within, again reflecting the tendency towards projection, which is encouraged by society and its respect for 'authorities' and 'experts', especially in the health fields. However, the major challenge of self-help, especially as regards health, is assuming the responsibility to become, and acknowledging that you are, the ultimate authority on yourself. Indeed we would all be experts if we allowed ourselves to do this, rather than expecting others to.

Sigmund Freud and other psychotherapists have perpetrated a disservice in this regard, by reinforcing the notion that they alone can interpret the meaning of images produced in dreams, day-dreams and fantasy. However – and this cannot be emphasised strongly enough – this is simply *not* the case. Others may be able to *assist* a person in understanding their imagery in a number of ways, some of which were used by Freud and his followers. These include helping people to explore how they feel about their imagery, what responses it evokes within them, and what associations it conjures for them. This may require some form of externalisation such as painting, sculpting, drawing, dance or acting; or it may need to be amplified in other ways, by another person expressing the responses the image elicits in them, including other associations, or pointing to the significance of similar symbols in mythology and elsewhere. Essentially this approach was that of the psychiatrist Carl Jung who insisted that, although a person's imagery may have certain universal features, it represents none the less the unique symbolic language or representational system of the individual, which they must learn to translate and understand. Accordingly, the interpretation of a person's imagery by another, however 'expert', will reveal only the features of the symbolic language of the latter, rather than that of their subject, and as such may be highly misleading. Therefore no one should allow others to impose meaning on their imagery or seek explanations of their symbols in the many publications that claim to provide them. Rather, they should explore their own symbolic 'vocabulary', its meanings and usage, much as they might discern the meaning of an unknown or unusual word or code: by examining its context, other available cues, similar sounding words, patterns of usage, the associations it evokes, and identifying its source or component parts in foreign or ancient languages. Individuals can thus build up an understanding of their own use of symbols, and become an expert in their own symbology. If they work with others in this enterprise they should ensure that the meaning of their personal symbolism is not lost in its translation by another.

Individual differences in the meaning of symbols may be highlighted in the water visualisation, which is particularly appropriate to matters of physical health given that the human body is 80 per cent water, and that both the human body and water are essentially different forms of energy.

Attention to specific features of the imagery may reveal potentially significant insights into personal energies and their utilisation.

Colour

Colour has always played an important role in healing traditions since the earliest times, and much of its significance is only now being rediscovered as a result of increasing investigation of subtle energies and their effects on organisms.

Colour imagery may be an important indicator of health and susceptibility to illness (for reasons which will be examined later). Predominant colours should therefore always be noted as and when they occur in association with imagery, together with any changes in these features over time.

Some colour imagery may strike an individual as odd or puzzling. For example, whenever one young woman imagined water it was always red, and its significance eluded her until she verbally associated the colour with anger. She could then recognise how much of her energy was bound up in this emotion.

One man imagined himself as brown water, which held no significance for him until he was asked how water becomes brown. After considering various possibilities he concluded that it contained material in suspension, decaying matter, effluent or sewage, and that it corresponded with his view of himself as 'all churned up' and 'full of shit'. Another man who imagined brown water saw it as an indication that he was 'bogged down'.

One woman described her water as 'murky grey and horrible', fouled by Canada Geese; while another imagined a bath of cloudy grey water, in which other people had washed their dirty clothes. This triggered an association with the phrase 'washing dirty linen in public', and she recognised that her present bad feelings arose from becoming involved in other people's unpleasant business, and allowing her thinking to become clouded by it.

Commonly people report that they imagine oily or greasy water, with a 'film' on its surface, which is once again suggestive of something having been 'dumped' or imposed on them from elsewhere. Most people are able to identify the source of this problem, the effect it is having on their energy, and how they can rid themselves of it.

Clarity

As these examples show, features of colour and clarity are often closely interrelated, but they are not necessarily so. The degree of clarity may be an indication of the insight a person has into herself. Some imagery suggests that an individual has only a very superficial awareness of herself, viewing her water from above, perhaps from a helicopter or aeroplane, and with no idea of what is underneath the surface. Some people are 'cut off' from their water – and possibly from themselves – viewing it through glass.

Many are able to see clearly through the water and identify its contents and boundaries. They can often identify these as significant issues in their lives, or as problems. Problems are often represented as features that the water has to overcome, circumvent or is obliged to encounter in some way. The size of these features may be indicative of the scale of the problem. Thus while some people 'flow' easily over or around small stones and pebbles, and support fish or other things without difficulty, others imagine themselves dashing against cliffs or beaches, pounding piers, jetties and other structures that have been imposed on them.

Unclear areas may indicate unexplored or unacknow-ledged aspects of the self, fears, anxieties and other features which people don't wish to look into too closely – their darker or shadier aspects. One woman saw herself as a shallow part of a river where stepping-stones had been laid. She 'saw' children playing in her, and although she felt pleased to see them enjoying themselves, she nevertheless felt resentment at being 'walked all over'. She recognised that she had more depth beyond the stepping-stones, in an area shaded by a willow tree, but felt reluctant to explore these 'uncertain' areas ahead. This suggests an avoidance of future possibilities and a disinclination to go beyond the present, despite her ambivalent feelings about it.

In some cases these dark areas may be a reflection of shadows that people perceive looming over them, and thus an indication of problems or negativity. Some people report being unable to see into their water because of reflections. This suggests the possibility that their reflection of other things or people, such as the expectations of others, prevents them seeing their own depths and potentials. Indeed, for many people all their energies are taken up in creating or living up to the images expected by others.

Depth

Many people don't see their depths or extent very clearly, but have an awareness that the water they imagine is part of a bigger expanse of water and that they have a far greater potential than they recognise or are using. While some are aware of drawing on inexhaustible sources, others see their sources as very limited, as a puddle or trickle. They may be unable to 'see' any source or any destination, suggesting no clear idea of 'where they have come from' or 'where they may be going'. Attention to the clarity of the water thus tends to highlight the features of depth and limits or boundaries.

While some people become aware of their hidden depths or unknown potentials, others recognise that their surface features give a false impression of what is going on underneath. In some cases the surface of the water may be calm and belie a churning underneath, or the surface may be very agitated, rough, wild or chaotic, but tranquil below. This may reflect the way in which some people, consciously or unwittingly, conceal themselves, and thus the difference between their inner and outer selves. It may be suggestive of powerful feelings beneath the surface or of a great deal of energy or potential, sometimes submerged at great depth. Individuals will therefore differ in their interpretation of and attitude towards the possible significance of their imagery.

Movement

The movement of the water is usually determined to some extent by the nature of the limits and restrictions upon it. Whereas some people picture their water as expansive, others perceive it as very confined, and often these restraints are man-made. Swimming-pools, fish-tanks, garden ponds, baths or even tumblers of water are imagined, which suggest rigid, artificially created restrictions. People frequently express frustration or anger at being hemmed in by artificial or natural constraints. One woman described feeling annoyed at seeing herself as a swimming-pool full of people, and realising that most of her energy went into supporting others. Another was alarmed to see herself as a static pool alongside the London orbital motorway, the M25, and to find life rushing past and herself going nowhere. Some find that they are streams or rivers confined to narrow channels, or canals. One woman who saw herself as a stretch of the Manchester ship canal realised she was confined by the environment of

47

the inner city. One young man, a student, saw himself as a powerful river cutting a downward V-shape into solid rock, which was taking all his energy but achieving nothing, as he was not going forward, but at a dead end. He recognised that the 'depression' created in the rock corresponded with his psychological state. Some people see themselves as bursting their banks, 'welling up', spilling out or flooding their surroundings, or as widening their boundaries; and others may be alarmed to find that they are shrinking, diminishing, evaporating or seeping away. One woman reported seeing two images – one which came 'unbidden' – a deep pool of still, blue water, which transformed into a muddy, shallow stream and then a trickle when she consciously tried to change the first image into something more 'interesting'. The image elicited considerable emotion in her as she recognised that all her life she had been 'trying and getting nowhere' and that this drained all her energy.

For the majority of people the most striking and significant feature of their imagery is the movement of the water. It may be stagnant, static, sluggish or slow, suggesting insufficient energy; or rushing, gushing, frenzied, overwhelming and, in some cases, dangerously out of control. Dissipation of energy is a common feature of imagery. So, for example, some people see themselves as a waterfall whose initial impetus is lost, peters out, or collects in a static pool. Water may disappear underground, into a hole or well, sometimes remaining underground, sometimes reappearing, or maybe vanishing without a trace. Inconsistencies in flow may be highlighted in this way, suggesting fluctuation in energy, or differences in the way it is being used. One man interpreted his dry river in a chalk landscape as reflecting his need to withdraw into himself from time to time to restore his energy. One woman saw herself as waves bobbing up and down, going nowhere. This she reported as agreeable when she was 'on the up' and her 'head was above water', but frightening when she was overwhelmed or 'down', and that this corresponded to her mood cycles.

Questions

From the examples given above it may be seen that frequently this exercise provides many insights into the features of a person's life, especially those which take up energy or prevent energies being used effectively. The new perspectives afforded by this different mental mode often highlight issues that people were previously unaware of, together with their implications for health and illness.

Commonly, therefore, the exercise prompts people to ask questions about their lives and ways in which they can make positive changes. It may give insight into the causes of illness or other problems, and the means of cure or solution.

Other questions commonly asked are rather more specific, for example, what is the purpose of counting 'one' during the relaxation procedure?

The method for eliciting the relaxation response devised by Benson derives from the TM technique, which is a traditional mantra meditation. Mantras are phrases or sounds which when repeated help 'switch off' the normal verbal mode and thus facilitate the emergence of the non-verbal or unconscious aspects of mind, and promote absorption. Counting progressively (one, two and so on, as in counting sheep), maintains the verbal and numerical modes and tends to accelerate these mental processes – thereby having exactly the opposite effect to that desired. 'One' is also similar to OM, regarded as the ultimate mantra, because when intoned properly it is believed to be the synthesis of all sound. Sound is, of course, vibration of a particular frequency – energy of a certain character. Like ancient man, modern physicists recognise all phenomena as energy, their different forms reflecting their varying vibrational character and the principle of resonance – that like affects like. As body organs have different characteristic frequencies, mantra theory holds that they can be stimulated or energised by vibrations of similar frequency. Accordingly OM is believed to energise all the organs and parts of the body and thus to enhance the effects of deep breathing.

Two frequent questions are how many times should you do this imaginary exercise, and will the results be the same each time?

All of the exercises in this book can be performed as frequently as you wish. As the exercise indicates the overall energy status of the person, energy blocks, and how effectively energies are being used, it can be used to monitor and regulate these factors. The insights thus derived can be used to modify behaviour, so that if one's energies seem to be 'running away' or drained, or dangerously out of control, they can be consciously conserved or controlled. The exercise may be used to identify physical energy blocks, to relax them, and also to examine the mental and psychological tensions that give rise to them.

Because the images are providing insight into aspects of the self, they will tend to reflect changes within an individual and the circumstances of his or her life. Nevertheless, certain features may remain constant for reasons which will be addressed in the next chapter.

Perhaps the most important questions, however, are about how imagery provides information about the body or emotions, and whether it is valid and reliable.

These issues will also be addressed in the following chapter.

3

MOBILISING THE HEALING POWER OF IMAGERY

Listen to the secrets that your blood whispers to you.

Hermann Hesse

One of the functions of imagery is that it provides a new way of looking at issues. This new perspective can afford insights which may be of value in everyday living, problem solving and especially in relation to health and illness. Healers since the earliest times have recognised the value of imagery, but today many people are reluctant to accept images as valid and reliable indicators in these matters. Yet modern brain research lends support to the claims of the ancients.

Imagery and brain function

When viewed from above the human brain looks rather like half of a shelled walnut. Its outer surface, or cortex, has two halves or hemispheres, which, although apparently separated by a deep fissure, are actually joined by a band of dense tissue composed of nerve pathways along which impulses are transmitted from one hemisphere to the other.

Although appearing the same, the two hemispheres of the brain are known to control different functions. During the last century the left hemisphere of the brain, which controls the right side of the body, was found to be primarily responsible for speech, language and related processes, which are characteristically linear, sequential and analysable or reducible into constituent elements. The processes of the left brain can therefore be thought of as logical, rational, deductive and analytic, and its expressive mode as verbal.

By comparison, the right hemisphere of the brain, which controls the left side of the body, has executive control over physical and emotional functions, including physical co-ordination, spatial awareness and the recognition of patterns and faces. It is therefore largely concerned with non-verbal processes and its expressive mode is the image. It can be characterised as intuitive or imaginative, holistic, integrative and inductive.

The functions of both hemispheres are necessary to health, and normally they are well co-ordinated. Even so, the left brain has definite advantages over the right. By virtue of its control of language and speech it has a voice which articulates much of our thinking and renders its processes conscious. To a great extent, therefore, we are aware of its operations. A further advantage is that Western society lays particular emphasis on the left-brain functions of rationality, reason, logic, analysis and verbal skill, and encourages their development through education and its scientific, technological culture.

By comparison the right brain has no 'voice' as such, with the result that we are largely unconscious or unaware of its functions; and Western culture tends to place little emphasis on intuition, imagination and emotionality, which are characteristically devalued as 'feminine' traits. Art, music, dance and other non-verbal forms are also typically ignored to a much greater extent in the West than in Eastern cultures, where what might be thought of as right-brain functions are more highly valued.

Clearer understanding of the value the West places on left-brain functions can be gained from attitudes to the effects of stroke or cerebral haemorrhage. Those individuals who suffer a left-brain stroke may experience loss of control over the right side of their bodies to varying degrees, and in extreme cases complete paralysis, together with some degree of verbal impairment. For many, loss of language function is more distressing than the physical disability incurred, not simply because they are handicapped in their ability to express themselves, but because others tend to assume that people who cannot speak properly cannot think or comprehend adequately either. Similarly, dyslectics and those with general difficulties in relation to the written word are often regarded as unintelligent. People who suffer from any of these conditions tend to be viewed as mentally deficient or stupid.

Right-brain stroke victims do not lose language functions, however, and so tend to be regarded as less handicapped. But the loss of functions that they experience can be equally or more distressing, and even more incapacitating. As a result of impaired spatial awareness, physical co-ordination and imagery – notably body image – they may be unable to perform even the most simple tasks such as dressing themselves and brushing their teeth. They may be unable to find their way around their own home and may fail to recognise members of their family. Impaired imaginal functions may result in memory loss, difficulties in thinking, planning and co-ordination of activities, problem solving and emotion. Thus, although frequently regarded as relatively fortunate, these incapacitated people may think they are going mad, which can be highly distressing.

A good deal of understanding about brain function has come from so-called split-brain research. This arose, and gained its name, from attempts to confine severe epileptic seizures to one hemisphere of the brain by surgically cutting the connective tissue between the two halves of the cortex. In such cases neural transmission is severed, and what might be thought of as communication between the two sides of the brain is cut off.

Although this surgery proved effective in restricting the severity of epilepsy, it has other rather less desirable consequences, notably that the individual effectively has two independent brains controlling his body, and to a great extent the left hand really does not know what the right is doing, often with bizarre consequences. Furthermore, emotion and personality are adversely affected.

Indeed, as a result of research in this and related fields, it is now clear that the right brain is directly involved in the control of emotion and has profound implications for personality and behaviour. Studies have shown lack of emotion, inability to hold symbolic imagery, little or no dreaming, dim waking imagery and inability to function on visual, auditory and olfactory sensory tasks in people with right-brain injury and surgically induced lesions such as pre-frontal leucotomy (Graham, 1990). It also seems clear that, because of its responsibilities for physical functions and emotion, the right brain has a direct relationship with the autonomic nervous system, that part of the nervous system which controls the involuntary actions of the smooth muscles, the heart and the glands. These connections with autonomic and emotional functions suggest that the right brain may have a key role in matters of health and illness, and that imagery may be significant in this regard. Modern research findings are consistent with both propositions.

Emotion and illness

A good deal of evidence indicates that suppression or denial of emotions such as hostility, aggression, depression and guilt, and the inability to express them, along with rigidity and impaired self-awareness, are all associated with cancer. An association between breast cancer in women and the need to 'get something off their chest' is widely recognised. Differences have been found between people with benign and malignant tumours in their expression of anger, long-term survivors finding it easier to express hostility, anxiety and alienation than short-term survivors (Siegel, 1986).

It has also been shown that patients who express emotion freely and show active determination to fight their illness live longer than compliant or defeatist types. Cancer patients tend to hold resentment, to be unforgiving and to have a poor self-image. Indeed, it would appear that the belief systems of those who succumb to cancer are essentially negative.

Recognition of these tendencies has led to the suggestion that there is a cancer-prone personality, but evidence in support of this claim is mixed. It would seem that cancer patients are no different from those who suffer other serious illnesses. Indeed, a number of studies suggests a common pattern of helplessness, hopelessness and resignation in both psychological and physical disorders. So, for example, women with rheumatoid arthritis tend to be tense, moody and depressed, and to deny anger and inhibit its expression.

Clearly, normal functioning and the maintenance of health would seem to require the co-ordination of all mental, physical and emotional functions, and thus effective communication between the right and left sides of the brain. Physiologically this is achieved by neuro-transmission of biochemical impulses. However, this does not explain how people become conscious or aware of unconscious emotional and physical processes, which is necessary if they are to acknowledge and express them. In other words, how do the non-verbal processes of the right brain become intelligible to the left brain?

Imagery and illness

What might be thought of as right-brain messages concerning physiological and emotional processes, health and disease are non-verbal and can only be processed into meaningful thought and made 'conscious' or verbal if translated by the left brain. Similarly left-brain 'verbal' messages have to be transformed by the right hemisphere into non-verbal terminology before they can be understood by the involuntary or autonomic nervous system.

Modern research suggests that this translation process is achieved through imagery, which serves as a bridge or mediator between the two sides of the brain and their different functions (Achterberg, 1985). This being the case, severance of connections between the right and left brain might be expected to result in 'untranslated' messages that would continue to affect emotions and alter physiology but without rational interpretation. That this does occur is suggested by the disorder Alixithymia – literally meaning without words or feelings. In this condition, emotions and images that are untranslated find expression physically in various body systems, and may eventually be diagnosed as rheumatoid arthritis, ulcerative colitis, asthma, hives, migraine and other so-called psychosomatic disorders.

Although this condition is not fully understood, it is thought to result from lesions in the neural pathways between regions of the cortex and the limbic system. The limbic system derives its name from words meaning 'border', and can be regarded as a 'border area' between the two sides of the brain, apparently the translation area for imagery. Interestingly, it corresponds in both position and function with what was known in ancient traditions as the 'third eye', which was considered to be concerned with insight, intuition, imagination and clairvoyance (literally 'clear seeing'). It would seem, therefore, that whereas the left brain, by virtue of language, may be thought of as the interface between the inner and external worlds of the person, the right brain, through its imagery, may be regarded as the interface between the different inner worlds of the self, and hence a valuable source of information about this realm.

It follows that where this bridge or link is little used, effective communication within the self is unlikely to occur and illness may result, either psychosomatically in the sense of untranslated emotional messages being expressed physically, or somatically (that is, bodily), because warning signs of disease are not recognised or acknowledged. Evidence suggesting that is the case comes from studies of Type A persons, cancer patients and those who suffer from rheumatoid arthritis or other 'psychosomatic' disorders, who typically are found to have poor visual imagery.

It may be, therefore, that one reason why they fall ill is because they are handicapped in their ability to interpret non-verbal cues relevant to health and, as they do not recognise signs of potential disorder, they cannot take appropriate preventative action. Alternatively, they may simply dismiss these cues as 'irrational', and ignore them. In either event, their internal communication is likely to be inadequate, with the result that they may be thought of as out of touch with significant areas of their personal functioning.

Imagery and health

Imagery may prove important to health in a number of ways: in facilitating the development of internal communication or self-awareness it promotes integration, or health in its true sense of 'being whole', and may provide early warning of problems and ways in which they can be avoided or overcome. It also enables communication of these insights to others, and thus may assist in both diagnosis and treatment.

There is little doubt that representation of various aspects of the self through imagery can be an important tool for self-discovery and creative change. Long before lateralisation of brain function and its relevant physiology were understood, ancient healers were aware that imagery offered a potent means of exploring the dynamics of mind and the discourse between mental and physical mental illness – applications which have been only recently rediscovered in Western medicine.

Sigmund Freud recognised the importance of the unconscious or non-verbal mind in illness, and imagery as a major source of information as to its contents. Like the shamans before him, he regarded the imagery of dreams as most important, describing them as the 'royal road to the unconscious'. He tried to access this imagery in diagnosis and treatment by examining his patients' dreams and fantasies. He took the view that the images were a facade behind which meaning lies hidden.

His contemporary, Carl Jung, also recognised the importance of imagery, describing it as the language of feeling. He disagreed with Freud, however, in viewing the image as not in any way deceptive, but as expressing something as best it can, although this may not be recognised by the individual through self-deception or lack of insight. He therefore avoided the theoretical approach for which Freud is renowned and focused on helping people understand their imagery without the application of any dogma. He claimed that the only way to fathom these inner processes is by paying close attention to fantasies, day-dreams and dreams, amplifying them in whatever way seems appropriate and committing them to memory. He saw externalisation of imagery through drawing, painting, sculpture, dance and drama as a means of amplifying the symbolic content, and communicating it to others, in order to facilitate further clarification and understanding.

He regarded the imagery spontaneously generated by the individual as the most valuable source of information about their inner life. However, some people find it difficult to generate imagery, and many therapists have recognised that suggesting symbols or images and encouraging their exploration as fully as possible acts as a trigger or stimulus, enabling people to project aspects of themselves into this material. Within this different representational mode they can access features of themselves of which they were previously unaware, helping them to find novel ways of dealing with their problems.

One way in which spontaneously generated imagery may be accessed, or in which stimulus-imagery can be suggested, is hypnosis.

Hypnosis

Most people think of hypnosis as a trance-like state in which the subject loses awareness and, controlled by the hypnotist, becomes able to perform a variety of feats that are normally impossible. This view is perpetuated by popular writers, the media, stage performers and professional hypnotists; and by dictionaries, which typically define hynosis as a special state of mind, resembling sleep, characterised by extreme suggestibility. Such a view is highly misleading. During hypnosis the subject does not lose awareness. If anything, their awareness is enhanced. Many people experiencing hypnosis for the first time are thus inclined to think that it isn't working, although its effects are clearly demonstrable. Moreover, the feats performed under hypnosis are achievable under normal conditions and, as well-established psychological processes can account for these effects very adequately, the notion of a special 'hypnotic' state is unnecessary.

Those who have witnessed apparently exceptional feats performed during stage hypnosis may dispute this. However, incidents where people have lifted a vehicle single-handed to release someone trapped underneath, although certainly uncommon, are not unknown and in the Herald of Free Enterprise ferry disaster a man effectively became a human 'plank' – an effect frequently demonstrated by stage hypnotists – thereby enabling others to walk across him to safety.

Indeed, there are many indications that feats of strength

and endurance normally considered to be impossible can be achieved when 'conscious' control of bodily processes is suspended or removed, and that under such conditions other apparently remarkable effects are possible, including pain relief, anaesthesia and organic changes such as the removal of warts.

Hypnosis appears to achieve its effects in much the same way as relaxation, that is, by helping people let go of the constraints normally imposed on the mind and body by rational, conscious mental processes. In so doing it puts them in touch with the unconscious mind – those features of themselves of which they are normally unaware – thereby enhancing their self-awareness and enabling them to influence directly physiological processes normally beyond their control. As in the case of relaxation, this is achieved primarily through imagery and facilitated by people's belief in the authority or expertise of the hypnotist and their willingness to comply with his or her suggestions. These suggestions are, in effect, directed not towards the individual's loss of control as such, but towards the loosening of the rigid control that their conscious mind normally exerts over their being. As such the person is not in any sense handing control over to the hypnotist, but, rather, gaining greater control of their own functions. Hypnosis can therefore more properly be thought of as guided self-hypnosis.

Hypnotic induction

Hypnotic induction is in most respects similar to relaxation procedures. It usually commences with the subject sitting or lying comfortably and having her visual concentration trapped and held by focus on a fixed point or object. This serves to strain the eye muscles, quickly inducing sensations of heaviness in the eyelids and their closure, which may be encouraged by suggestions of heaviness. When the eyes are closed, relaxation is achieved through attention to breathing and the release of muscle tension in various parts of the body. This may be augmented by counting backwards, or by imaginary exercises such as descending steps. A relaxing scene is then suggested, which the subject is encouraged to imagine as vividly as possible, and when she is deeply relaxed, suggestions relevant to a desired objective are introduced.

Under these circumstances many effects, including regression, amnesia, pain relief and anaesthesia, can be demonstrated, and for this reason hypnosis has been widely used in surgery and is frequently employed in dentistry.

Experimentally it has been demonstrated that the pain-relieving effects of hypnosis are equivalent to those of morphine (Stern *et al.*, 1977), which suggests that it may enable the person to produce endorphins, the natural opiate-like pain-killers of the body. It is used extensively to control pain, anxiety and insomnia in the treatment of cancer, and to overcome nausea, anticipatory emesis and other effects of chemotherapy.

Hypnosis has also been shown to be effective in the treatment of asthma, headache, skin conditions, high blood pressure, peptic ulcer, bedwetting, backache and insomnia; and to help overcome addictions, smoking, overeating, obsessive-compulsive behaviours and depression.

Subjects are frequently trained to achieve these effects by inducing hypnosis themselves and introducing suggestions designed to bring about psychological or physical change. These suggestions may be in the form of verbal directions, for example, 'My hands are heavy and warm', or 'I will say "no" each time I am offered a cigarette'; or in the form of images, which are frequently more potent as they do not require translation and can influence right-brain processes directly. It has been demonstrated that many physiological functions, such as heart rate or stomach contractions, can be speeded up or slowed down through suggestion, and that distant vision can be improved by suggesting changes in the shape of the eyeballs (Schultz and Luthe, 1961). It has recently been shown that women receiving positive suggestions through headphones during surgery for hysterectomy recover significantly more quickly, suffer less pain, require fewer pain-killers and are discharged from hospital earlier than those who receive no suggestions (Richardson, 1988). It is also being recognised that suggestions made to the patient by the surgeon during an operation may have a significant effect on the patient's recovery and well-being. Increasingly therefore, the role and applications of both hypnosis and suggestion in health and illness are being explored within orthodox medicine.

The following exercise combines elements of a hypnotic induction technique with specific imagery.

Exercise 3
Imagery facilitated by hypnotic induction

Lying or sitting comfortably, either close your eyes or focus them on a fixed point or object, and begin silently counting backwards from 300. Do not concentrate on distracting thoughts, simply let them go, and return your attention to counting downwards, matching your breathing to your counting.

Imagine that you are descending some steps and, on each one, you are progressively letting go of a little more tension in the muscles of your body, so that you are becoming more and more relaxed. When you have done this, imagine that it is a warm, sunny day. You are somewhere on the coast, but between you and the sea there is a high sea-wall, so that although you can hear the sea and smell it, you cannot see it.

Walk along the bottom of the sea-wall and you will come to some very steep stone steps – ten in all – set in the wall. You begin to climb them, mentally counting each one as you do so; but they are very steep indeed, and the effort involved is considerable, so much so that you pause on each one and take a deep breath.

On the fifth step you pause for a slightly longer period, breathing in deeply because of the effort. Your limbs are heavy with the exertion.

You continue climbing the steps, mentally counting each one as you do so and pausing on each to take a deep breath. You reach the top of the sea-wall and pause. Breathing in deeply, you smell the sea, which is now visible beyond an empty expanse of sand. There are no people on the beach or in the sea, only a few gulls and wading birds. This pleases you, and you remain for a few moments more enjoying the solitude and the warmth, the sights, sounds and smells of this unspoilt place.

You walk a short distance along the sea-wall and discover ten steep steps leading down onto the sand. You begin to descend them, silently counting each one as you do so, and, once again, you find yourself pausing on each and taking a deep breath as you feel the increasing heaviness in your limbs, and the increasing warmth afforded by the shelter of the wall. Upon reaching the sand you find that its warmth combined with the heat reflected from the sea-wall makes you warmer still, and you begin to walk across the sand towards the sea.

The sand is very fine and your feet sink deeply into it, so that walking requires a good deal of effort. The feeling of heaviness in your legs spreads throughout your body, and you feel progressively tired, so much so that you lie down on the warm sand. You spread yourself out, arms and legs apart, and you immediately feel the warmth from the sand below and from the sun above.

As you sink into the fine sand, you feel comfortable and relaxed. The tensions in your body appear to melt and dissolve into the sand as you lie looking upwards for some moments at the almost cloudless sky.

You find that your eyes are closing, and as they do you become aware of the smell of the sea, and you inhale deeply several times. You become aware of the taste of sea-salt on your lips, and of an intermittent fine sea-spray on your body. You become aware of the sound of the sea and the movement of the waves, and as you do so you match your breathing to their ebb and flow. As you breathe in you hear the inward rush of the water as it breaks on the shore, and with your out-breath the sound of the water being drawn back across the sand.

Silently you begin to count each cycle of movement, counting 'one' for each time a wave breaks on the shore and is drawn back into the sea.

Whenever your mind wanders you note the thought or sensation that arises, but, without holding on to it, allow it to drift out to sea on the next wave, and return to your counting.

Your mind gradually empties of thoughts, preoccupations and concerns, leaving you relaxed in mind and body, and feeling tranquil and at ease.

As all thoughts fade, the image of a rosebush comes to mind, and you recognise it as a symbol of yourself.

Pay careful attention to it, noting all its features as vividly as you can. Notice first its surroundings, and details of climate, light, shade and such like.

Then pay attention to the plant itself. Notice first whether or not it is in flower or bud, or is fruiting, and the size, colour and condition of these features.

Notice also the leaves, their size, colour and condition, whether healthy, diseased or pest-ridden. Notice the stems, their colour, number, strength and condition, and any thorns there may be.

Notice how the plant emerges from the material in which it is growing and the condition of that medium, whether rich or poor in nutrients and water.

Then look down into that material, following the roots of the plant, and noting their every detail, especially their depth and extent. When you see every detail as vividly as possible, look at the rose in its entirety. Ask yourself what this image says about you and your current situation. How healthy is the rosebush? What does it lack? What does it need? How would you describe its outlook?

When you have answered these questions, allow the image to fade. You are once again aware of lying on the sand. The tide is coming in and the warm, clear water is lapping at your feet. You lie there enjoying this sensation until the water is gently washing over your entire body. Imagine it washing over and through you, refreshing you in mind and body, removing tensions and pains and cleansing you of all impurities, toxins and disease.

Feeling fully revitalised and energetic, healthy and well, you open your eyes and stand up. You begin to walk briskly, easily and effortlessly towards the sea-wall. Finding the steps there, you ascend them quickly and without effort, counting them as you go. Reaching the top of the wall you pause briefly to take a last look at the sea. As you do so your attention shifts to your breathing, the image of the sea fades, and gradually your awareness returns to your surroundings and you open your eyes.

Take time to record your experience and any insights derived from it, in the first-person present tense, and remember to note the answers to the questions concerning the rosebush.

Commentary

Some people claim not to be able to 'do' this exercise for a variety of reasons, which are often highly significant in themselves.

They may claim not to like the sea, sand or sunbathing, or to be frightened of the sea, and so unable to relax and 'get into' the exercise.

This highlights the power of the conscious mind to control a person's experience, even at the fantasy level, so that his preconceived view limits even his imaginary experience. Others think they may be being hypnotised and resist, once again reflecting the limits their expectations and beliefs impose on their experience. It also indicates rigidity, in the sense that these individuals will not allow themselves to imagine a different response or to create a new experience for themselves, which is significant given the part played by rigidity in illness and problem solving.

Some people resent the 'intrusion' of the rosebush, reporting that they were happy and content where they were on the beach. This suggests complacency, reluctance to change or to admit new experience, to progress or to deal with the unknown.

Others state quite simply that they cannot imagine a rosebush. Rather than merely accepting that this is the case, it is important to examine what is stopping them doing so.

Men typically have more difficulty in this regard than women. Examination often reveals their view that a rosebush is 'sissy' or unmasculine. This in itself is significant, as it reflects their stereotypical assumptions about what is and is not appropriate: the kinds of 'shoulds' and 'should nots' or restrictions they impose even on their most private experience. These limiting factors often create tension and generate illness, and prevent them dealing effectively with their problems. Inability even to imagine a rosebush because of its possible feminine connotations suggests a very frail masculine identity.

Some people are aware of consciously trying to modify their imagery, usually when they do not want to acknowledge or accept the image that arises spontaneously. They invariably find that the original imagery resists all attempts to change it, obliging them to pay attention to it. Indeed, any aspect that someone wishes to change or finds hard to accept should be examined closely, as it invariably represents repressed features of that person, which may have important implications for his or her overall well-being.

In some cases people find that another plant impresses itself on them and resists all attempts to be modified into a rosebush. Where this occurs, it is usually because this image more adequately conveys the person at that time, and attention should be given to the specific features of this image that may be difficult to accommodate within the rosebush theme. For example, one man found that he saw a marsh marigold, growing in water, which was a very apt metaphor for his view of his life situation (he was emotionally 'waterlogged' and began to cry as he revealed this), but would not be consistent with the normal habitat of a rosebush. Others may see large trees on a scale very different from that normally found in a rosebush. Here size or bulk may itself be a very significant metaphor for the person or some feature of his or her life.

This raises the question of the purposes and adequacy of the rosebush imagery. Certainly any image would serve as an effective stimulus for the person to unconsciously project into. However, a plant is particularly suitable because it is a natural, dynamic, organic entity that grows and develops and is sensitive to environmental factors. For this reason, plant analogies are much favoured by philosophers and teachers, including Christ, who frequently used them in his parables. Flowering plants, in particular, feature in traditional symbolism throughout the world, where they typically represent the development of the whole person rather than any one specific aspect. Indeed, the very complexity of a flowering plant makes it a useful analogue of the person at many different levels. The rose is especially versatile in this respect because of its range of colour, form, habitat, universality, scent, and its thorns.

The rosebush imagery affords the opportunity for people to represent many features of themselves in a novel way, including those aspects of which they are normally unaware or unconscious, and thus facilitates new insights and different perspectives on issues. The overall context or atmosphere in which the rose is situated may reveal the way people view the situation in which they find themselves, and thus their outlook on life. The fruiting and flowering parts of the plant may suggest the extent to which their potentials have flowered or borne fruit; those aspects of themselves that are yet to come to fruition; or those that have been 'nipped in the bud'. The colour, shape and number of the flowers and their condition may be significant, as might the specific features of the leaves.

The stems may provide some indication of how much

support or strength people see themselves possessing, and the degree of confusion, or chaos, in their lives. There may be a good deal of dead wood, or new growth, various entanglements, restrictions, or undergrowth, which may be significant. Woody growth and thorns may reflect people's defences, and provide some idea of the threats they perceive to their well-being.

The medium in which the rose is growing and how the plant emerges from it are usually good indications of how secure or well grounded people are. The roots may also reflect this, along with their present or past experiences and relationships.

For many people the insight into themselves afforded by this exercise is very profound and quite unanticipated. One woman recognised in her inability to see a rose, despite a clear picture of its surroundings, her lack of self-image and awareness. This spurred her to seek therapy, during which she recognised many repressed features of her self and her life and their involvement in her physical illness. Yet another woman was alarmed to find her rosebush completely overwhelmed by other plants, with only one feeble flower managing to 'keep its head above those around it', and recognised in this the way her identity had been submerged and almost lost in rearing her family. Subsequently she began to attend to her own development, by introducing changes in family routines and making her children more self-sufficient.

A young woman saw a rose that was quite perfect except that it was 'completely wound up in itself', while in a different case a rose that appeared perfect in every respect was subsequently acknowledged as being, like its 'creator', completely alone and lacking the closeness of others, for which she yearned. One woman imagined her rosebush being 'undermined' by sheep eating its roots. Another saw her rosebush set in a small, shallow bed surrounded by crazy paving, which prevented the roots going wide or deep, resulting in an unstable plant that had to be supported by a thick stake. She recognised in this the insecurity arising from an unhappy childhood and the need to establish secure roots and a stem strong enough to forego external support.

A man suffering acute depression as a result of the loss of both his job and his marriage imagined a large rosebush with a great deal of old growth and large thorns. He recognised in this just how much he was hanging on to his past, his defences, and to the belief that he was too old to 'start again'. He also realised that by cutting out the dead wood he could promote new growth, and bring colour back into his life. This awareness gave him hope and was the turning point in his successful recovery.

One of the most dramatic examples of a person regaining hope through this exercise came from a young woman who, as the single parent of a profoundly handicapped child, faced enormous social, economic and personal difficulties, together with health problems. When she initially performed this exercise her rosebush reflected her despair and depression, being completely black and without flowers or buds of any kind. A couple of weeks later she was obliged to withdraw from the course because of the imminent death of her daughter, but she sent a message to the group, to say that she was well and coping and that her rosebush had produced one pink rosebud.

One of my early experiences with this exercise convinced me of its potential for promoting self-awareness and change. I had produced the image of a container-grown rose that had been placed in a marquee the night before a large flower show. I could readily appreciate the significance of the container and the situation, as these reflected key features of my life at that time, but I was absolutely amazed to discover that my flowers were of a quite different colour than they 'should' have been. I 'knew' myself to be an orange rose, but the flowers I could see were pale mauve in colour. I became quite agitated by this, as no attempt on my part would bring about the desired change in colour and this led to my becoming angry about being a 'forced, hot-house rose' and the circumstances in which this had occurred. A good deal of emotion was thereby generated, but even though this in itself was meaningful and of value, I could not discern the significance of the 'wrongly' coloured flowers and my emotional reaction to them. It wasn't that I didn't like the mauve flowers. On the contrary, I thought them most beautiful and attractive. It was the conviction that they 'weren't me', and that the orange flowers were preferable, that was disconcerting.

Despite a lengthy attempt to do so, I could not fathom this feature of my imagery, and it continued to plague me for weeks. Then one morning I awoke knowing exactly what my imagery meant. I 'saw' in my mind's eye that the 'orange' flowers I insisted were my true colours were in fact the 'rusty' colour of dead roses, and I realised that I had been holding onto an outmoded and inappropriate view of myself, and failing to acknowledge changes in myself. The effect of this awareness was to enable me to stop resisting my own growth and the development of my potentials, which I realised had manifested both emotionally and physically as tension.

This experience also highlights other features of imagery exercises. The experiences tend to stimulate a good deal of thought long after the exercise is over, which in itself often yields further insight, but also tends to stimulate other unconscious processes such as dreaming. It is therefore not unusual to encounter the same motif or symbols in subsequent dreams, day-dreams or fantasies, or to discern their meaning as a result of these other activities. A dream may thus yield a further understanding of a previously unfathomed image, just as an imagery exercise may clarify the content of a dream. Indeed, it would seem that once somebody opens up the 'bridge' between the conscious and unconscious aspects of herself, the unconscious will take any opportunity to use it, and so dreaming typically becomes more frequent and more vivid, and impresses itself more powerfully on the individual. The entire imaginal system seems to develop and become elaborated.

I have been asked whether imagery comes more 'naturally' to women than men. The ability to produce imagery is 'natural' in both sexes, but in men its use and rehearsal is more overlaid by cultural factors, notably the insistence that they should be rational and logical. It is only relatively recently that women have had access to similar educational opportunities, and even now they are less likely to pursue scientific and technological subjects, and more likely to develop more creative, artistic potentials. As a result, their intuitive powers are less constrained and more evident. Nevertheless, their intuition, irrationality, illogicality and emotionality, while tolerated, tend still to be regarded as comic and dismissed as greatly inferior to male rationality and logic. However, recognition of the importance of intuition and creativity in scientific and business endeavours has led to greater emphasis being placed on it in training programmes. Acknowledgement of the role of visualisation in improving performance in physical activities has also led to its widespread use in sport, which remains male dominated, and to its investigation by sports psychologists.

The implications for health and illness of the differences in socialisation of men and women are examined in the following two chapters.

4

RECOGNISING HEALTH NEEDS

You don't get tired of what you need.
Patricia Wentworth

The rosebush exercise affords new perspectives on the self at a number of different levels. In particular, it may highlight the individual's unmet needs for sustenance, nourishment, warmth, enrichment, culture, care, encouragement, contact, support, organisation, control, 'pruning', space or change of situation, as well as various obstacles to the fulfilment of these needs. These features are of relevance to health and illness.

Needs and health

The term health has its source in words meaning 'whole' and 'holy'. Etymologically, therefore, it encompasses the whole person, physically, psychologically and spiritually. This concept is central to the view of Abraham Maslow, a distinguished professor of psychology, who was concerned to promote the study of the whole or healthy person. He indicated that health must be viewed as the fulfilment of physical, psychological and spiritual needs.

He conceived of a hierarchy of needs, basic to which are physical needs for water, food, air, light, warmth and sleep. He observed that these must be met before psychological needs for contact, safety, love, attachment, identity, relationships, sexual fulfilment, intellectual and other achievements, respect and prestige are fulfilled. Thus a person suffering from starvation, chronic thirst or lack of air is unlikely to be too concerned about his popularity or prospects for promotion.

70

Similarly, psychological needs have to be met before the individual can address their spiritual needs for meaning and purpose in life. Maslow saw illness as the body's way of telling the person that important physical, emotional and spiritual needs are not being met. He regarded man as having an inner drive towards growth and health, which is easily frustrated, denied and suppressed, giving rise to physical and psychological illness. He thus regarded self-denial as a major cause of psychological illness and distress.

Clearly, illness is likely to occur when physical needs are unmet. Without the basics of food, water and sleep the individual will fail to thrive, and is likely to succumb to illness. Similarly, failure to meet psychological needs may manifest at the psychological level as neuroses, or at the physical level in so-called psychosomatic disorders. The psychotherapist Frederick Perls also saw health as the satisfaction of needs. He insisted that it can be achieved only through the integration of all the parts of the self, because it is only in this way that the self emerges as unified or 'whole' in relation to its environment and is able to assert or express its needs and satisfy them. The attainment and maintenance of health therefore requires constant monitoring or aware-ness of the self and redefinition of its contact boundaries with the environment, which, rather than being fixed or static, are dynamic and ever-changing as the demands of the self, others and the external world alter.

Accordingly, the satisfaction of one's various needs is something of a balancing act, maintained by a self-regulatory process of constant awareness of the self and its situation. The aware individual is able to perceive changes in the overall pattern of himself and his world and act accordingly to create new patterns, thereby restoring the equilibrium between the self and its surroundings. Health may therefore be thought of as adjustment or balance.

Like Maslow, Perls attributed much of the difficulty in maintaining this balance to the way individuals are required to conform to one central, enduring social role, and the expectations that attach to it. In being simply a male or female one is obliged to suppress, disown or project onto others and the environment all the features of oneself that are inconsistent with the maintenance of that role. Accordingly, males characteristically suppress the more sensitive side of their natures, and thus certain emotions and their expression, intuition and aesthetic qualities, whereas females typically fail to assert their independence, aggression, sexuality and intellect. This denial of self invariably results in a progressive fragmentation of the person, and a difficulty in establishing boundaries between the self, others and the external world. Consequently individuals experience confusion as to where they end and others begin, and cannot satisfy their needs as they are not aware of what they are. Such confusion may ultimately lead to complete disintegration or breakdown – physical, psychological, or both. By comparison, survivors have been found to have a clear hierarchy of needs, and unlike most people, pursue all of them, thereby functioning in a holistic or healthy manner. Furthermore, they do not act in isolation or with disregard to others, and not thereby from self-interest but in the interests of others, even in the most stressful of situations. Their needs thus go beyond self-actualisation to synergy, where the whole is more than the sum of the parts.

Needs and illness

Perls viewed psychological and emotional disturbances, or neuroses, as the inability to perceive boundaries clearly, resulting in people experiencing the world as encroaching on them. Not surprisingly, therefore, the neurotic is characteristically fearful, and his anxiety manifests in phobias, avoidance tendencies and elaborate defences, all aimed at avoiding this intrusion, and also physically in tension and stress-related conditions. Being unable to define personal boundaries, that is, the self, the neurotic individual is unable to satisfy his needs and remains in a state of psychological disequilibrium that may be thought of as 'unbalanced'. Moreover, because he cannot define himself, the neurotic cannot be self-reliant, and tends to manipulate the environment for support in a number of ways, one of which is illness.

The psychiatrist Joseph Berke observes in his book *I Didn't*

Have to Go Mad Here that illness invalidates what can be thought of as the social contract, the tacit agreement which defines the terms on which social responsibility is delegated to the individual by the state and its institutions, and the terms on which it is assumed. If the contract is broken by either party it becomes invalid. Therefore 'invalidity', or being an invalid, is one way – perhaps the only socially acceptable way – of breaking the rules and not accepting the responsibility proffered. Thus, as Berke indicates, the person with a 'nervous breakdown' does not necessarily have anything wrong with their nervous system, nor does the term necessarily reflect the degree of emotional stress they may be experiencing. Rather, it denotes a situation whereby a person with no obvious physical disability refuses to carry out their personal and social obligations, requiring others to do so. From this perspective, much illness is a retreat from responsibility, and sickness a legitimate means of rule breaking.

Psychosomatic illness may also be a way of obliging others to take over one's responsibilities, and meet one's needs. This can be dramatic, as the following example illustrates. A married woman with a full-time, demanding job and a family intermittently suffered such excruciating backache that she was completely immobilised, obtaining relief only after several days' confinement in bed. This situation had continued over many years since her marriage and seemed quite inexplicable, no physical cause of the problem being found despite extensive medical investigations and tests.

During the exercise described later in this chapter, she suddenly realised that the attacks always occurred a few days after an argument with her husband about his failure to do his share of the household chores, and that as a result of her 'condition' he had to take over the running of the household completely. Backache was therefore a very effective way of 'getting back' at him, and was not so much a medical condition as one of the implicit conditions of the marriage contract.

One man's misery at 'being back' from his thoroughly enjoyable holiday in the sun manifested in an agonising and debilitating backache, which justified his depression and

73

inability to resume work.

In the course of another workshop, a woman realised that her hospitalisation for surgery resulting from breast cancer was the only way in which she could get away from the difficulties she experienced in her relationship with her daughter. After approaching these issues by way of visualisation, she was able, for the first time ever, to acknowledge and express her dislike of her daughter and her need to be distanced from her. Once she had 'got this off her chest', her cancer began to regress and eventually disappeared.

Another woman, whose profound hearing difficulties resolved themselves spontaneously three weeks after the death of her husband, recognised that she had remained in a very unhappy marriage for over forty-five years only because she had been able to 'turn a deaf ear' to her husband's demands.

In a culture where feelings are regarded as being of little importance, emotional needs are frequently ignored and illness can provide a way of meeting needs that a person is otherwise unable to fulfill. These needs may be for space or time for oneself, freedom from duties and responsibilities or from relationships. It is a socially acceptable way of not fulfilling various functions and jobs, and it makes it easier to say 'no' to unwelcome duties or tasks. It may also give someone permission to do things she has always wanted to but has never had time for, or it may be an excuse for failure. Illness is often the only way that a person can ask for help or love, or express unhappiness. Illness therefore gives people permission to allow themselves and others to do things they wouldn't if well, and to do so without guilt, the need to explain or justify.

The extent to which illness is used as a means of self-justification is generally given little attention. However, in a work-orientated culture with an emphasis on productivity, there are no 'well days' that individuals can take off from work or study in order to relax, avoid stress and potential breakdown. The only way for many people to take time off is to be sick or pretend that they are. Frequently the guilt and anxiety generated by the latter produces actual illness, so at best this strategy ensures the person derives little benefit from the break in normal routine, and at worst proves totally counterproductive. For the housewife and mother, staying at home provides no respite whatever, and so 'well days' are often impossible. The only way to take a break may be to take to one's bed.

Illness usually functions as a message to change, or provides us with something we are not otherwise getting from our lives. As such it can be a temporary and a useful respite, but it may be a trap for those who find it is the only way in which they can gain attention, love or release from tension, and avoid stressful and unpleasant activities. For such people permanent 'disability' may be more attractive than the alternative. However, the benefits of illness, whether mental or physical, may not be consciously recognised, much less acknowledged by the sufferer. The 'meaning' of much illness is thus frequently ignored. However, closer scrutiny invariably reveals that it is an outer manifestation of some inner turmoil.

This awareness was the basis of the healing tradition established by the Ancient Greeks, from which all Western medicine derives. They viewed health as essentially a spiritual phenomenon, with all human problems, physical or psychological, being seen as symptomatic of *psychopathology*, literally sickness or disease of the soul. Treatment was therefore directed to the cure of the soul, or *psychotherapy*, through restoration of balance and harmony. The same principle is discernable within the psychological medicine of more recent times.

The psychiatrist R.D. Laing regarded much mental illness as spiritual in origin. He insisted that it is often a sign, not of disintegration, but of an attempt at reintegration into the larger whole, a spiritual striving often misunderstood, misrepresented and thwarted. Victor Frankl, Carl Jung and Roberto Assagioli are among many noted psychiatrists who also view mental illness as a failure to find meaning in life, or to acknowledge and satisfy spiritual needs.

Jung recognised that spiritual needs were of particular importance, claiming to have seen no patient over thirty-five years of age whose problem was not, in the final analysis, one of not having found a spiritual outlook on life and thereby meaning.

75

Recognition of needs

Within the fields of psychiatry and psychotherapy there is widespread acknowledgement that failure to meet physical, psychological or spiritual needs may result in physical or mental illness, and in a great deal of pain, discomfort and distress, not only for the individual concerned, but also for those around them, much of which could be avoided if their needs could be met in other ways.

The problem, as Perls has indicated, is that many people are unable to express or act on their needs because they are not in touch with them and so do not know what they are. Frequently they mistake wants for needs, and fail to recognise that the two are not necessarily the same. A want *may* indicate a need: wanting a dishwasher may indicate a person's need for more time free of domestic chores; wanting a foreign holiday may indicate a need to get away from it all and relax; and wanting a new car may indicate a need for more status and self-esteem. However, wants often conceal needs, or are a rationalisation of them. Thus a person may know they need a break from the children, or a respite from work, but feel guilty about this and so convince themselves and others that they *need* a labour-saving device or a weekend cottage. Frequently when they get what they want they find that it doesn't meet the need. Sociologist Ann Oakley has pointed out that labour-saving devices such as vacuum cleaners, washing-machines and dishwashers invariably increase the amount of housework. Before their advent a certain amount of grime was accepted as inevitable, whereas now standards of cleanliness have risen to virtually clinical levels, exerting constant pressure on individuals seeking to conform to them.

Sometimes wants bear little or no relation to needs. Most of the commodities advertised in glossy magazines can easily be lived without, as can the contents of the increasing number of unsolicited home-shopping guides which are distributed by mail to almost every household. A recent 'buyer's guide' offered, among other things, a Teddy-bear car alarm; a model vintage-car desk ornament 'personalised' with the buyer's name; a 'personalised' cat flap; a gravity inverter (a device for standing a person on his head); a 'squeaking' T-shirt; and a cash box disguised as a can of soup. Headlines such as 'the only shoulder-pads you'll ever need' (featured in the same publication) encourage the belief that these items are a necessity and are invariably unquestioned by the reader. Indeed everyone is conditioned into believing they need what other people want them to. Other people's wants are imposed on the individual throughout life, from childhood onwards. Parents tell their children they *need* sleep because they want a few hours free of them; that they *need* to eat their dinner because they don't want to throw it away; that they *need* some exercise because they want them out of the house on a Saturday afternoon; that they *need* a good education and a career because they don't want to support them financially for the rest of their days. Men are told they *need* jobs and sex, women that they *need* men and children; men that they *need* success in their work to be fulfilled, and women that they *need* marriage and a family.

It is therefore not surprising that many people find it difficult to distinguish their needs from other people's wants or to perceive how much of their time and energy are taken up with the latter.

Accessing needs through imagery

In many cases people are out of touch with their needs because they have inadequate inner dialogue and therefore take insufficient notice of messages concerning physical and emotional matters.

Contact can be established and developed through visualisation, and needs accessed thereby. The following exercise, 'the magic shop' – from which this book gains its title – is directed towards the recognition of needs and their discrimination from wants. Over many years I have found it to be one of the most powerful and versatile in the healing repertoire, often yielding dramatic insights, resolution of problems, and personal transformation. It employs guided fantasy, a method first used by shamans to lead their clients through the landscapes of their imagination and reintroduced into psychotherapy in the 1930s.

Guided fantasy

Guided fantasy can be linked to a waking dream, a process whereby a person, guided by another, creates in the imagination a new experience for himself. It can be thought of as a situation where a 'storyboard' is provided for a 'movie' in the mind, which the individual casts, enacts, produces and directs himself. Its purpose is to provide the person with a means of representation which had previously been lacking or inadequate, and which challenges his existing representational mode. It is therefore most appropriately employed where someone's normal way of representing issues is inadequate for coping in a given area.

Through guided fantasy the person can confront the contents of his personal unconscious and relate them directly and often dramatically to his problems. By exploring his own symbolism and transforming or translating it, he can make contact with the generally unrecognised aspects of himself and thus effect a healing, or integration. As guided fantasy tends to be highly absorbing, it generally promotes relaxation, and so preliminary relaxation procedures are usually unnecessary.

Exercise 4
The Magic Shop – a guided fantasy

Take a few moments to make yourself comfortable and to withdraw your attention from your surroundings and bring it to your inner self, closing your eyes as you do so. Imagine it is the late afternoon of a day towards the end of the year and you are shopping in a familiar street. It is dark and the shop windows are brightly lit and full of vivid and colourful displays.

As you are walking along the street looking in various windows, it suddenly begins to rain very heavily, and looking about for shelter you see an opening which you may or may not have been aware of previously. You step into this opening and, having done so, glance back into the street from which you have come, briefly observing the scene there.

Then you glance down at yourself, noting your appearance, clothing, sex, age, and how you feel. When you have done so, you begin to explore your surroundings, your feelings, and reactions to them. Looking ahead your attention is drawn to what appears to be a shop window. You approach it and peer in, noting what, if anything, you expect to see there, what you do see, what, if anything, you are particularly attracted to, and how you feel about it.

As you are looking in the window you become aware of a doorway to one side, and as you turn to look at it the door opens and a figure appears in the doorway, and beckons to you. Responding to this gesture you approach the figure, noting every detail of its appearance as you do so, and how you feel towards it.

You follow it over the threshold, and the door closes behind you. The figure then communicates to you in some way that you are in a magic shop which contains the entire universe. You may have whatever you want and take it away with you on condition that you leave something in its place. The figure then withdraws, leaving you to browse around the shop.

Take time to look around the shop, noting what you see or experience there, and what you don't see or experience that you might have hoped or expected to. Take note also of whatever you are drawn to, and why, and what considerations influence your choice.

After a while you again become aware of the figure urging you to make your choice, if you have not already done so, and reminding you that you must leave something in its place.

Having made this transaction, you become aware that you are being propelled towards the open shop door. You find yourself outside the shop, and the door closes behind you and disappears from view.

Take note of how you feel, and looking down at yourself observe your appearance.

When you have done so, walk back towards the street from which you first came, and then back into your present surroundings. Then take a few moments to record your experience in as much detail as possible, and in the first-person present tense.

Commentary

Unlike previous exercises which present a single, static image, the guided fantasy is very complex. Apart from the basic 'storyline' every feature of the fantasy is the individual's own creation, and as such potentially very meaningful.

The significance of some features will be immediately obvious but others may need considerable work for their latent meaning to be discovered.

In a workshop situation the participants may be paired and asked to relate their experiences to their partners in the first-person present tense, noting the key features and their feelings about them. The listener is then encouraged to assist in uncovering the meaning of the experience by amplifing its content in various ways, such as indicating 'missing' elements of the story, or those which are only sketchily described; asking about the feelings associated with each feature; inviting associations – of words, thoughts or memories – and offering their own associations and suggestions (but *not* interpretations); and encouraging the person to draw or paint features of his or her imagery. The whole group then examines each of the key features of the fantasy in some detail.

The 'opening' scene

The shopping place and/or the opening in which the person seeks shelter may or may not be familiar. The latter may be a side-road, alleyway, doorway, subway or shopping mall, but irrespective of whether or not it is open to the sky the person invariably reports that it is not raining there, in contrast to the street where it is still raining, and that it is daylight. This is some indication that 'conscious' control of the process has been relinquished, because, were this not the case, one might expect the conditions in the street and in an area open to the sky to be much the same.

Some people immediately feel anxious on leaving the street, suggesting a fear of the novel, unexpected or unknown, and a few experience anxiety reactions such as sweating, trembling or goose-flesh, which indicates the effect of imagery on physiological processes. Many rationalise this reaction in a number of ways, for example as a fear of being mugged, raped or assaulted. This is in itself significant because they have produced this scenario as opposed to non-threatening alternatives, and, to the extent that they are unable to change it or its inherent possibilities, it suggests a rigidity of expectation or attitude which is essentially negative.

The fear may be quite unspecific, and indicative of unconscious factors that may limit ordinary behaviour just as they constrain fantasy activity. Many of those who experience anxiety will overcome or endure it, while others will be unable to do so and will go no further. Were they to do so they might well find that other features of the experience would highlight their fears, anxieties and concerns.

People are often startled by the discovery that in this fantasy experience their appearance has altered. They may find that they are wearing strange or unfamiliar clothes or costumes; items of dress they do not possess or have never owned; or clothes from earlier stages of life or periods in history, or different cultures. Their sex, age, skin colour, race or ethnic character may also have undergone change, as might their height or weight. These features are symbolic and need to be explored if their meaning is to be discerned. Notwithstanding their personal significance, they also indicate that conscious control has been relinquished. In some cases this awareness prompts an immediate reaction, often panic or fear, and an attempt to restore conscious control by censoring or directing the ensuing imagery. Again this suggests a certain rigidity in the person's mental operations or representational mode, and a dis-ease with the less rational features of the self.

It is not unusual for people to find themselves minus items of clothing, or even body parts. Some, when looking down at themselves, can see no body at all. This often reflects a poor body image or a poor sense of self. Missing feet and legs may indicate lack of security or 'groundedness', or their 'poor standing' in the world. In Perls' terms, these individuals may have difficulty in adjusting to new situations or change, and in establishing their personal boundaries or self in relation to their environment. It may indicate that they have a tendency to be overwhelmed by situations, and to lose themselves as a result.

Other aspects of the setting may also be significant, especially if they promote strong emotional reactions, and should be examined more closely.

The shop front

The shop and its window are, for most people, the most salient aspects of their surroundings. Shops of every conceivable kind emerge in varying degrees of illumination and clarity. Their windows may be well stocked, or empty, featuring only a single item, or a few, some or only one of which attract attention. The contents may be clear or vague, difficult or easy to see or sense, and they may give rise to various feelings, thoughts, memories, associations or past experiences. When examined in more detail it is frequently the case that the window and its contents reflect the person's wants, albeit represented in symbolic form. These may correspond to the contents of the shop and to what they eventually take from it, but usually they are totally different.

The 'shopkeeper'

The figure in the doorway is a key feature of the fantasy, standing as it does at the threshold of the shop and thus symbolically at the threshold of the person's inner self. It may be a friend, foe or family member (alive or dead), or an unknown person; a fictional, fairytale or mythological character, creature or animal; a film, television, comic or cartoon figure; an inanimate object or one, such as a skeleton, strangely animated.

There may be no figure as such, only a feeling or vague sensation: a light, colour, or indistinct form. The clarity of the figure is greatly variable. Some are perceived in vivid detail, while others may be hooded or concealed in some way, or have no discernable features of any kind. In some cases the figure spontaneously changes identity or form, or may be a kaleidoscope of different images or impressions. Irrespective of its appearance, people are usually emotionally moved by it in some way. Reactions vary enormously from delight and great happiness to sadness and fear. Frequently people experience spontaneous outbursts of emotion, and can be perceived crying, smiling, frowning or laughing.

Usually the figure relates to the person's needs – often unmet needs, especially in respect of unfinished business and past relationships. Hence dead or distanced relatives, friends, lovers, teachers, business and social acquaintances or pet animals commonly appear. Many people are astonished to encounter a person they haven't thought of, much less seen, for many years, and they cannot understand why they should do so. Similarly, people may be perplexed to find themselves in the company of Mickey Mouse or Mary Poppins, and it is important to remind them that it is not necessarily the character *per se* that is important but what it symbolises or represents. Thus, while for one person the figure of his mother may represent some matter directly relating to her, for another the mother figure may signify an aspect of his childhood or later experiences; past or present aspects of his life; particular issues, problems, feelings, situations or conflicts; or it may symbolise motherhood, caring, nurturance, submissiveness, repression or hardship. Sometimes the significance of the figure may be discerned only after a lot of hard work.

Sometimes a specific feature of the figure can be puzzling. An example from my own experience may illustrate this. In one of my 'journeys' to the magic shop I was baffled to find my doorkeeper attired in a long white apron. I realised I would not have produced this were it not in some way significant, but its meaning continued to elude me despite my attempts to understand it. Much later, after producing various associations, I realised that it was a cobbler's apron, but this did little to clarify the meaning, until I asked myself what a cobbler does, and came up with the answer 'he mends soles'. The pun was not lost on me, as I recognised immediately that my doorkeeper was in fact involved with the repair of *souls* – psychotherapy – a significant issue for me at that time, as I was planning to write a book on the subject. However, a former student provided an alternative interpretation of the imagery, that is, that it was simply 'cobblers'!

The shop interior

Once in the shop many people find themselves drawn immediately to particular objects, such as televisions, cars, stereograms. This materialism is very evident in some people, especially the young. Others, particularly older people, are drawn to more abstract qualities such as love, peace, tolerance, health; or to objects which they recognise as symbolising these. Some take an object, often against their inclinations, only to discover subsequently that it represents a more abstract issue of which they were unaware at the time.

For example, one woman was puzzled to find herself choosing a grand piano, which of all the things in the universe she could have chosen seemed to her to have a very low priority. When asked if she was musical she said only that she had been. However, several days later she remembered that on the death of her husband two years previously she had sold the piano along with some other furniture, and had not realised until prompted by the magic shop exercise how much she needed the self-expression it had afforded her. The awareness proved so powerful that she immediately purchased another piano. Yet for another woman in the same group the choice of a saxophone was in no way related to music, it being her symbol of freedom.

Some people enter the shop with a very clear idea of what they are looking for, and may be disappointed if they don't find it. In some cases they fail to see anything else, which indicates how desires can often limit one's vision and prospects for fulfilment or satisfaction. Others, having seen what they want in the window, are then surprised to find something in the shop which they need or value more. One woman, on entering what had appeared from the outside to be a shop containing domestic appliances, was surprised to find it was a very dark church, badly in need of illumination. She realised that this indicated her need for 'enlightenment' and that her spiritual aspect had been neglected.

Some people find there is *no-thing* they want. The experience enables them to realise that they are not really concerned with material possessions, and that many of their everyday wants are not needed. Others recognise that even their non-material wants may not be what they need.

One person became so convinced that all he wanted was the 'shopkeeper' – a fantasy character for whom he felt great affection – that he went into the shop, protesting as he did so, only when obliged to by the shopkeeper. He was then struck immediately by what he 'needed' – an intimate, loving relationship with a real person.

Some people find what they want, but then fail to strike a bargain because they feel they should make an equivalent exchange and can find nothing of equal value to leave in its place, as in the case of the woman who left the shop empty-handed because she had not had time to assess the value of the item she had chosen. This may reveal the way in which their codes of conduct or morality lead to self-denial, or how other self-imposed 'shoulds' and 'should nots' limit their chances of fulfilment. A graphic example of this was provided by a young woman who realised she needed space, which was symbolised for her by a large house. However, her religiously inspired principles of self-denial led her to reject this and leave the shop, apparently with nothing. Back on the street she was horrified to find that she had become a 70-year-old 'dried-up' and lonely monk with a begging bowl, and she immediately recognised in this the 'poverty' of her moral principles and the consequences of her self-denial.

Some make exchanges only because they feel they have to. They believe they must do as they are told, follow instructions and abide by rules. They may take something they don't particularly want or need because they can't find anything else or don't particularly want to look. One young woman, finding few material items in her shop, felt cheated to 'have' to come out with a bottle of shampoo, the best of what was on offer. She didn't want to consider any possible significance it might have, such as her needing to 'wash something out of her hair', or other suggestions made to her. She said she found the shop boring and merely did as she was told. When asked if she normally did this, she said she didn't know, and that the questioner would have to ask her husband! The clear implication of her response was that he knew her mind, and presumably her wants and needs, better than she did.

It may be difficult to accept that the offer of anything in the universe could possibly be boring. However, the universe of some people is unbelievably restricted, being confined to the known, certain and habitual, and lacking all novelty, challenge, excitement or interest. Such was the case for this woman, who reported that she had expected her shop to be boring, and it was, providing a clear example of self-fulfilling, albeit in this instance self-denying, prophecy.

One young man was annoyed to discover only one item in the shop, and therefore only one choice – take it or leave it. He took the item, feeling resentful as he did so, and only realised later that it was something he needed but might not have recognised or taken away if given more choice.

The tendency not to seize the opportunities presented or to make the best of them, to be inhibited by doubts, indecision, scepticism, negativity and guilt may be highlighted in this exercise, and help individuals to understand the consequences of these attitudes. Frequently those who, for whatever reason, 'look a gift-horse in the mouth' feel depressed, disappointed, upset, angry, regretful, resentful, or older, darker, heavier afterwards; and these traits may characterise them and their reactions to everyday life.

Negativity may be expressed even more dramatically, as in the case of the man who gave both of his legs in exchange for the resolution of past relationships; and the woman who exchanged her health for a semi-precious stone and imagined herself to be so weak that she could hardly return to the main street.

While some people fail to make an exchange because they have nothing of value to leave behind, there are others who are reluctant or refuse to give up what they have. This in itself may prove highly revealing when examined in detail. One woman, whose long-term uncertainty about whether or not to seek a divorce had led to physical and emotional difficulties, found on entering the shop that she wanted her husband as he had been when she was first married to him, but not enough to give up anything. Initially she reported that she had nothing to exchange for him, although when questioned she admitted that she had thought of leaving her inexpensive handbag, but had decided against it. This shocked her because it suggested that she didn't regard her husband as being of much worth, which she knew was not the case. However, when asked about the importance of her handbag, she declared that it meant 'everything' to her and that she 'would be lost without it' because it contained her Filofax full of business and social engagements – precisely the things she would have to give up if she remained in her marriage. She recognised that her uncertainty about the marriage arose because she was holding on to an outmoded and idealistic view of her husband, just as he was holding on to an unrealistic view of her as a housewife and mother who should be content to stay at home. As a result she chose to 'save' herself rather than her marriage.

By comparison, some people conduct their transactions easily and strike very positive deals, exchanging items or features of themselves or their lives that they don't want or need for ones that they do. These individuals get maximum value from the exercise, often finding immediate solutions to their problems, feeling rejuvenated, lighter, brighter, better, healthier and happier as a result of the experience. For many the insights are profound, as in the case of the man who left behind his illusions, having recognised them for the first time, and the one who realised that his struggle to choose between two alternatives in his life was quite unnecessary. Such people are generally positive in attitude and outlook, and make the best of the opportunities they create or that are presented to them. They tend to enjoy new experiences and self-discovery, and to act on the insights derived thereby. Typically they appreciate the power of the 'magic shop' exercise in shedding light on significant aspects of themselves and their lives, and its potential for transformation, and will use it time and again.

Indeed few people fail to recognise the power and potential of this exercise, and as a result questions about its purpose and usefulness are rare.

5

ACTUALISING PERSONAL POWERS AND POTENTIALS

People become sick because they lead sickening ways of life.

Sidney Jourard

Many psychologists have emphasised the importance of self-actualisation or realisation. This can be thought of as the need to fulfill all personal potentials – physical, psychological and spiritual – and to attain thereby a total integration of body, mind and spirit, which is equivalent to health. However, this striving towards health is thwarted in various ways.

Social factors and self-actualisation

In attempting to conform to their central social role people tend to suppress or disown features of themselves, and in so doing effectively turn their back on much of their own nature, including their best features, talents, potentials and creativity.

Nationality and race may have significant implications for self-actualisation because to a greater or lesser extent they prescribe what shall be expressed and what repressed. Nations and cultures thus differ in the extent to which they encourage the development of personal potentials. In South Africa, for example, the majority of the population are repressed, and expression and development of their potentials are actively discouraged. Religion or creed may also be a significant determinant of self-actualisation. In Ancient

Greece, the source of Western culture, the manifestation of human potential was regarded as an affront to the gods, which led to the withdrawal of their support and protection, and was not encouraged. In the later religious traditions of the West, man was urged to project all his powers onto God. Practices which emphasised the development of human powers and potentials were seen as a threat to God and were systematically eradicated. Accordingly, in the West there is a tendency for people to devalue their talents and to fear that they may be punished for them. The actor Lee Marvin summed up this Western attitude rather neatly in his comment: 'White knights shine too brightly on the battle-field. They get knocked off easily'. Thus, despite Christ's admonition not to hide one's light under a bushel but to let it shine for all men, there is a reluctance to do so, potentials being viewed as threatening, and suppressed in various ways.

The religious traditions of the East have a very different emphasis. In the sense that God exists at all, he is viewed as a symbol of the personal powers of man which he should strive to realise in this life. The aim of Eastern religious traditions is therefore the achievement of the greatest potentials. Talents are seen as gifts of God, and their manifestation and development as the highest form of worship.

Irrespective of nationality, race, religion or creed, and so-called equality of opportunity, different patterns of life tend to be prescribed for males and females. Marriage is still the primary universal standard by which women are evaluated, as work or career are for men. Accordingly, males are encouraged to strive, to achieve in the world outside the home, to support others and to be 'breadwinners'. In order to do so they need to be competitive and assertive, and to suppress emotionality, vulnerability and signs of weakness.

These traits are encouraged in early infancy and reinforced during subsequent development. Boys quickly learn that crying and other signs of 'weakness' are unacceptable, that emotion should be controlled, and that strength and rationality are highly desirable. Their aptitudes and interests are channelled into technological and scientific endeavours, and away from artistic and aesthetic pursuits. This is reflected in male styles of dress, 'masculine' clothes typically being functional, practical and drab, making it difficult for the wearers to express their more aesthetic or sensitive features.

By comparison, females are expected not to strive or to achieve outside the home, but to confine themselves to the domestic sphere and depend on, or care for, others. As babies and children, their interpersonal sensitivity and emotional expression is encouraged more than physical activity, exploratory behaviour and curiosity. They are not expected to display intellect, initiative, independence, 'grit', 'pluck' or dynamism, and schooling generally reinforces these expectations by encouraging girls in domestic 'science', the creative arts and languages. Again this orientation is reflected in female dress which emphasises the decorative and aesthetic, rather than the functional. Thus attired it is difficult for a female to express the more practical side of her nature.

This restriction in the expression and development of potentials is increasingly being recognised as having implications for health and illness.

Social factors and illness

There is a marked tendency for men to succumb to stress conditions such as heart attacks and coronary heart disease, ulcers and gastro-intestinal disorders, which are a feature of the Type A syndrome. The indications are that in US suburban areas the Type A behaviour pattern is increasing dramatically. Moreover, the expectation that men are self-reliant, independent and strong often results in those who are most at risk dismissing the possibility, and failing to seek help (Hughes and Molloy, 1990). Not uncommonly men find relief in alcohol, as one of the few socially acceptable ways in which they can express emotions such as sadness, guilt and fear is to become maudlin with drink. Frequently, however, drink leads to aggression and violence, and thus reinforces socially accepted patterns of male or 'macho' behaviour.

Women are encouraged to express emotions and weakness, to be helpless and dependent on others, and these traits are frequently reflected in the illnesses to which they typically succumb (for example certain cancers and rheumatoid arthritis). Their use of drugs is also consistent with this pattern, tranquillisers usually inducing further passivity, dependence and helplessness. However, as women increasingly enter the same professional areas as men and are subjected to similar stresses, they more frequently succumb to the same diseases, and the same 'remedies'.

Traditionally, mental health has been seen as largely dependent on the successful adoption of the personality traits and behaviours considered appropriate to the individual's sex. This view owes much to Sigmund Freud, who claimed that passivity, dependence and nurturance are healthy female attributes, and that assertiveness in women is a sign of neuroticism. This view still prevails among many health professionals, so that the woman who insists on understanding the medication or treatment prescribed for her, or seeing her medical records, is likely to be labelled neurotic. Indeed the 1980 US Subcommittee on Drug Abuse indicates a clear sex bias in treatments prescribed for patients presenting stress-related conditions. Women, and housewives in particular, tend to be prescribed psycho-active or mind-altering drugs such as diazepines (Valium and other tranquillisers), whereas men with exactly the same symptoms are likely to be encouraged to take up golf or squash. The tendency to associate psycho-active drugs with female patients and non-psychoactive drugs with men is also clear in drug advertising literature. This implies that women experience emotional or mental illnesses, whereas 'real' or physical illnesses are suffered by men. Doctors also tend to attribute male symptoms of stress and anxiety to 'real' causes such as work, and women's symptoms, even if presented as physical, to neuroses. A female complaint is thus far more likely to be regarded as neurotic than that of a male. Doctors may reflect the cultural expectations about the sexes in other ways. It is therefore not unknown for general practitioners to recommend that a woman get herself a new outfit or hair-do to 'cheer herself up' – a very unlikely prescription for a male.

These assumptions about men and women in general medicine reflect cultural stereotypes of the sexes, and have very important implications in that standards of mental health differ for men and women. Whereas it is healthy for a man to adopt the characteristics or traits associated with his sex, an inverse relationship holds for women, because the 'normal' feminine traits of dependence and passivity are not positive correlates of mental health. Abundant research supports this observation (Broverman *et al.*, 1970). High levels of femininity have been found to be positively associated with anxiety and negatively associated with such indices of health as adjustment, autonomy and assertiveness.

Not surprisingly, therefore, women are significantly more likely to seek help or treatment for mental disorder than men, and exceed the latter in psychiatric out-patient clinics and hospital wards by a ratio of 2:1. Moreover, the conditions they suffer show consistent sex differences. Men tend towards conditions characterised by destructive hostility or self-indulgence, to be assaultative, impulsive and more inclined to acts of violence such as rape and mugging. Women, on the other hand, show higher levels of nervousness, insomnia, nightmare and confusion. However, the greatest difference is in the clinical diagnosis of depression, which is two to three times greater in women than men.

The rate of these disorders in women has been increasing in recent years, as has alcohol and drug abuse. Attempts to explain these findings in terms of biological or anatomical aspects of femaleness have a long history, but have largely proved inadequate. The most convincing explanations are, in the main, those which relate mental illness to the types of social roles that women are expected to fill. These explanations focus on two issues: what women are supposed to do, and what they are supposed to be.

Traditionally it has been assumed that a woman will be passive, emotional, dependent, nurturing, domesticated, low in achievement, unassertive, submissive and unintelligent, albeit a 'good' wife and mother. Accordingly she is expected to do the housework and domestic chores, low-value and low-status occupations, and to 'do' as a sex partner. It is not surprising, therefore, that much modern research has suggested that, far from being related to biological factors as such, mental disturbance in women is related to *marriage*.

Marriage and illness

Married women consistently report more depression than married men of equal socio-economic status, whereas single women report less. Housewives are particularly prone to depression, although depression is higher in both men and women when they have young children, and the younger the children the more depressed they are likely to be.

Other important predisposing factors for women are having three or more children under the age of fourteen, not having a job, the loss of their mother during childhood, and lack of an intimate, confiding relationship. One of the most common presenting patterns is the woman who feels that she is not a person in her own right, merely a mother and housewife who has no status because the needs of others are more important than her own. Much of this occurs because women are presented by the media with an idealised and unrealistic view of motherhood which they hold up as a standard.

By comparison, single women have far fewer emotional disturbances than either men or their married counterparts, despite the fact that their single status is often stigmatised. They also tend to report themselves as happier than single men, but less so than married women who work outside the home. Single women are also generally physically healthier than married men and women.

Thus, although marriage is used as a standard whereby women are evaluated, there is fairly consistent evidence that there are higher rates of mental and physical illness in married women than in those who are single, and higher rates of mental illness in married women than in married men.

Research shows that, in terms of mental illness, being married is considerably more advantageous to men than women, while being single is, if anything, slightly more disadvantageous to men (Brown, 1978; Gove and Tudor, 1972). Marriage thus presents particular stresses for women, a major one of which is confinement within the home.

Domestic bliss?

A consistent feature to emerge from contemporary research is that mental and physical health are poorer in women working within the home. Indeed, it has been suggested that housework is directly opposed to self-actualisation and personal growth because it provides no feedback about the self, no possibility of advancement, no intellectual challenge and, invariably, no recognition by others of the labours involved. At most it provides only a fleeting sense of accomplishment. Furthermore, it is often associated with some degree of social isolation and the demands of young children. Given these factors, it is perhaps less than surprising that housewives, as a group, show more symptoms of stress and depression than any other group of comparable age and socio-economic status.

This has led to a reappraisal of marriage by psychologists and sociologists, if not by the population as a whole. It is now clear that, rather than the idealised view presented in the media, marriage involves all kinds of cultural and personal expectations. These may include the assumptions that the women will do the housework, cooking and her 'duty' in bed, that all friends and social life will be shared, and so on. There is fairly clear evidence that these factors may be important in the development of certain disorders. For example, some 84 per cent of agoraphobics are women, 80 per cent of whom are married. Indeed, the onset of this condition normally coincides with getting married. It may be seen as a reflection of extreme sex-role socialisation, the women affected having not been encouraged to be independent or to master their fears of the environment, and generally experiencing low self-esteem relating to their low status in marriage and society as a whole.

There is also evidence that the social pressure for passivity in women may lead to their dependence on tranquillising and sedative drugs (Hewitt, 1986). It has been suggested that women's cultural conditioning towards helplessness, powerlessness and dependence is a major factor in predisposing them to neurosis, depression, anxiety and phobias. However, conflicts between conventional femininity and independence,

94

assertiveness and intellectual and vocational achievement may lead to stress and related conditions, and such ambivalence is thought to be implicated in various eating disorders and weight-related problems.

Role flexibility and health

From the foregoing it is easy to presume that the roles men and women play in society must invariably predispose them towards certain types of illness or disturbance. Arguably, however, there is nothing inherent in these roles that necessarily predisposes a person to illness of any kind – it is rather the way the person enacts the role, and the conditions under which he or she assumes it. This raises the question of choice, which governs not only the roles as such, but the way they are interpreted. Individuals may freely choose marriage without necessarily committing themselves to all its stereotypical features. Problems tend to arise when people interpret a role too rigidly, especially where they see the role in question as enforced or obligatory, and neither comfortable nor rewarding.

All the indications are that the debilitating effects of sex roles can be avoided through flexibility in their interpretation, and that those who achieve this are healthier, more adaptable and better adjusted than those whose behaviour is firmly rooted in the stereotypes associated with one or other sex. Similarly it has been found that satisfactory adjustment and health in old age are determined largely by role flexibility. Social psychological research clearly indicates that health is contingent, to a considerable degree, on flexibility of thinking, attitude and behaviour. It is therefore important in promoting health to cultivate fluidity, versatility, or what the psychologist Edward de Bono has termed 'water logic': a non-rigid, creative way of approaching and dealing with the features of oneself and one's life.

In so far as it creates a different perspective on personal potentials and talents, the following may be regarded as an exercise in water logic.

Exercise 5
Discovering hidden treasure

Sitting or lying comfortably in quiet surroundings, imagine that it is a warm, sunny day and that you are walking in an area of outstanding natural beauty. You have in your possession a diamond pendant on a gold chain which has been given to you because it confers protection and all kinds of powers, enabling you to perform tasks normally impossible. You walk, taking note of all the sights, sounds and smells of your surroundings, until you reach an expanse of water. Approaching the water's edge you find moored there an inflated dinghy, in the bottom of which are two oars.

You climb into the dinghy, unleash it from its moorings and, taking up the oars, row across the water until you are directly underneath the sun.

You take in the oars and, as there is virtually no movement of the water, the dinghy remains quite still. You lie back, resting your neck and head, arms and hands against the soft, cushioned sides of the dinghy, and as you do so you become aware of the gentle undulations of the water underneath, which is warm after long exposure to the sun. You feel as though you are lying on a waterbed, warmed from below by the water and from above by the sun.

You close your eyes and enjoy the sensation of peace and tranquillity. As you do so your physical tensions, aches, pains and discomforts are gradually soothed away, followed by your mental tensions, anxieties, concerns and preoccupations. After a while you are no longer aware of the dinghy. You feel as though you are completely at one with your surroundings. There seems to be no barrier between yourself and the water. It is as though you are supported by it, and moving gently in it.

Suddenly you become aware, with absolute certainty, that somewhere in the water there is hidden treasure which is yours. You sit up and look over the side of the dinghy into the water, noting what you see and how you feel; and then, pausing only to check that you still have the diamond pendant, you dive overboard and go in search of your treasure.

You explore under water, observing whatever is there, and your reactions, until you locate your treasure. Having done so, you inspect it thoroughly, using the pendant to assist you if this is necessary, and observing your reactions as you do so. If you don't wish to take your treasure on board, leave it where it is, and return to the dinghy, and then to the shore, noting your feelings and reactions, and your reasons for rejecting your treasure.

If you wish to keep the treasure, then take it back to the surface of the water and on board the dinghy, again using the pendant if necessary. Ask yourself what changes it will bring into your life, what you can and will do with it. Then, if you still want to keep it, row back to the shore, observing as you do how you feel about your treasure.

If you decide against keeping your treasure, throw it overboard, and return to the shore. Then allow the image to fade and return to your ordinary surroundings.

Take a few moments to record your experience, in the first-person present tense.

Commentary

The first feature of this exercise is the introduction of the diamond pendant, and reactions to it are usually significant, reflecting a person's typical attitudes and expectancies.

Some people report feelings of delight, safety, strength, power, confidence and excitement; others feel anxious, taking the view that if they have been given it for protection, they are likely to need it. Some fear its powers, or are sceptical about them and so don't trust it.

Thus while some people are positive in their attitudes, others betray negative attitudes and expectations. As in the previous exercise, this reveals those who tend to look a gift-horse in the mouth and fail to make the best of the opportunities they are presented with. Some people reject the pendant altogether; some modify it. It is quite common for people to devalue or cheapen it in some way, turning the diamond to glass and the gold chain to a cheaper material. This suggests a tendency in people to devalue their gifts. One woman described her pendant not as diamond or gold but as plastic, 'cheap tat'. Another dismissed it as the kind of item one might purchase through a cheap mail-order catalogue. One woman was convinced that the chain would break or rust. Others have felt they would lose it.

Sometimes people will reject the pendant because their 'conscience' dictates it. They feel they are unworthy of it, and closer analysis sometimes reveals this as a false modesty on their part. Others take the pendant but don't use it, or feel bad about it. Women occasionally think it won't suit them, that it is too elaborate, or not to their taste and style, suggesting a rigidity in their definition of themselves, their femininity, or what is appropriate for them.

Men may reject the pendant as effeminate, which again suggests the extent to which they may be limited by their attitudes and expectations. Some men hide the pendant – and thereby their potential – keeping it close to their chest, often quite literally, in the hope that no one will notice, irrespective of the fact that no one is looking!

For some people, both male and female, the pendant in itself is tremendously liberating. One woman found that it enabled her to overcome her fear and anxiety, which was sufficient 'treasure' in itself; so much so that when she found a hoard of rubies she didn't take them. Other women frequently report that the pendant is their treasure because it gives them the self-confidence they otherwise lack. Some time after having attended a workshop in which she was introduced to this exercise, a woman subject to attacks of agoraphobia found herself in the centre of a town and overwhelmed by anxiety. As she stood immobilised by fear she remembered the magic pendant and, imagining that she had it with her, was able to compose herself sufficiently to return to her car and drive home.

For one man the pendant enabled him to relinquish conscious rational control of his mental processes and to 'take off' into fantasy for the first time. To him this represented priceless treasure.

Even with the pendant, some people do not want to jump into the water because they fear the unknown, uncertain and hidden. Others report that they were enjoying the experience in the dinghy so much that they didn't bother to jump into the water. This reflects their complacency – the tendency to maintain the status quo and not 'rock the boat' – and invariably a fear of the new and of change. Some will deny this, often because they confuse complacency with being positive, whereas in fact it is usually quite negative.

One man, recognising that the pendant enabled him to shrink or fly, and wanting to do the latter, reported feeling disappointed at being required to enter the water and very reluctant to do so. When he did he was again disappointed by his treasure, an empty Coca Cola tin. His reaction to the exercise is suggestive of several features, for example a reluctance to look into himself, and the tendency to expect and experience disappointment (self-fulfilling prophecy).

For a lot of people the tendency to think about the situation in their normal way prevents them acting on it. Hence some people take the exercise literally and, because they don't like water or can't swim, don't pursue the imagery. This indicates the extent to which their ordinary experience, outlook and literal mode of thinking exercise control even over their fantasy, preventing new experiences and discovery of the hidden aspects of themselves. If they cannot allow themselves the freedom to explore these features in fantasy, what prospect do they have of allowing such freedom in reality?

Most people, including those with reservations about doing so, jump into the water and are usually surprised by their reactions. Some delight in the sheer freedom and pleasure of an experience that in real life they would never allow themselves. For many this is their treasure. Others 'treasure' the enjoyment of or fascination with plants, fish and colour.

Others remain or become anxious. One man described feeling very happy in the warm water until he remembered that sharks also enjoy it, and the resulting anxiety prevented him exploring further. He subsequently acknowledged that he was always looking for disaster, worrying about hazards, problems and difficulties, and that this typically prevented him from undertaking or attempting anything new, even activities that appeared attractive and pleasurable, and from enjoying much of the familiar. For one woman, however, the shark she feared ate her, although, like Jonah, she didn't perish, and this different perspective on her fears subsequently proved very valuable to her.

Some people see their treasure as soon as they look over the side of the dinghy into the water. Others have a definite concept of what their treasure is, and in searching for it fail to see what is actually there. One man was convinced that a woman in his group had taken his treasure, because she found what he failed to! Some fail to find treasure or don't recognise it as such when they do because of their prior expectations. Thus they claim not to have found anything except a stone, a feeling or a coloured light, and dismiss this or feel disappointed by it. Frequently these are people who dismiss themselves as 'only' this, or 'just' that, usually housewives.

There are also the 'doubting Thomases' who fail to find treasure because they 'never really expected to', perhaps because they 'don't deserve to', and those who simply lack vision and can't see anything at all. A few are so frightened they may find nothing, they don't even look. Others are disappointed upon finding, say, a treasure-chest to find it empty. They tend to interpret this as meaning they have no treasure. They often fail to see that there is space, room and air in the chest. Sometimes closer inspection reveals a lining, soft to the touch, such as red velvet, or leather; or other subtle features. In this way some people learn that their treasure can be *accessed* through touch, sensitivity or 'feelings', or that these qualities *are* their treasure.

Most people, however, find their treasure quickly and easily. They may recognise its significance immediately and react strongly towards it, the emotions elicited being many and various. Others may be perplexed by the discovery of 'treasure' such as a crumpled dead leaf, or an old boot, but feel quite certain that, for some reason, it is of value or importance.

Of those who find their treasure, there are always some who reject it, and their reasons for doing so are usually highly significant. One woman found life, but left it behind 'because you can't hold on to life', clearly indicating her despondency and lack of hope. Another woman saw a large clam and knew it contained her treasure but didn't look inside because she feared disappointment. Questioned about this she admitted that her fear of failure had always prevented her ever trying to fulfil the potential she suspected she possessed.

The tendency to devalue or trivialise treasure is usually very evident. Some people see theirs as cheap, or plastic. One woman, on finding a casket of pearls, used her pendant to shrink it in order to take it away, thereby reducing its size and value, rather than using the pendant to expand her capabilities to accommodate it.

Many people take only a small part of what they find, because they either 'can't carry it' or don't want to be greedy. Indeed some are alarmed by the size and value of their treasure, don't know what to do with it, and reject it because it will change their lives too much, or be too great a responsibility. This indicates a reluctance to change, which often lies behind self-denial or apparent acts of 'conscience'. Fear and discomfort are common reactions to the size of the treasure. Invariably it is women who are most threatened by awareness of the size and extent of their hidden talents and potentials. One was terrified by the vast genie that emerged from her treasure-chest, and slammed the lid shut, but not quickly enough to prevent her recognising what it was. Another didn't even look at her hidden treasure – a partly hidden building – because its steep roof thrusting upward from the lake bed hurt her feet, 'unsettling' her.

Similarly, women's treasure is more likely to be hidden, or heavily defended, sometimes by sea creatures, and in one case it was in the sealed vault of a sunken submarine which could be penetrated only by high-power drilling equipment. Some don't take their treasure seriously, and use this to justify their dismissal of it. This is often an indication that they don't take themselves seriously. One attractive young woman saw her treasure as a frilly black bra, which she put on and immediately felt mischievous and sexy in, but didn't want to 'take on board'. She recognised that in rejecting it she was dismissing her youth, femininity and sexuality, which she regarded as inconsistent with her student status and 'feminist' views.

Another woman rejected her treasure-chest full of vitamins because she considered it 'silly'. By comparison there are some people who realise, as did the woman who found the Monty Python team in underwater boats, that their treasure is a sense of humour, and the ability to appreciate the absurd and ridiculous aspects of life.

Many people fail to recognise what is of value, and therefore can't use it for the benefit of themselves or others.

One woman left her treasure because she regarded it as 'too common'. Another rejected the battered bucket she recognised as the one she had used to catch tadpoles in when a young child. She didn't examine it or pause to consider its possible significance, but merely discarded it. However, another woman seized upon her childhood bucket and spade with glee because of all the things she could make with it.

Another woman rejected a pile of 'thick, boring plates', realising only on returning without them that they were not plates but a stack of records. She was left pondering the question of just how much of her potential she had in the past failed to recognise because of her tendency to regard herself as 'thick and boring', and also her pattern of regretting lost opportunities. Other feelings prevent people recognising or exploring their hidden talents and potentials. Lack of confidence or lack of trust are common, as in the case of a woman who, upon seeing a castle (a good indication of well-developed defences and self-protection) rising out of the sea bed under her feet, lost confidence in her pendant and fled.

By this stage most people realise that the production of imagery is only part of the process of developing self-awareness, and that translation of its highly personal symbolism is necessary if an effective and meaningful inner dialogue is to be established. Many are beginning to recognise and understand elements of their personal symbolism, and the meaning of themes in which certain symbols recur. They are also becoming familiar with the process of amplification and increasingly using associations of all kinds, brainstorming techniques and also artwork and drawing in an attempt to discover the meaning of their symbols. Typically they are also beginning to identify characteristic attitudes and assumptions of which they were formerly unaware or have failed to acknowledge, together with their implications. Thus it is not uncommon to hear comments such as 'I'm doing it again, aren't I?' – whether 'it' is being negative, making assumptions, or avoiding the issue. Some recognise that because they expect something to happen, they act in ways that increase the chances of the expectation being met. So expectation of failure will often result in an unsuccessful outcome, which validates the negative expectation. The outcome thus created supports the validity of the original expectation – the 'I told you so' phenomenon – and the expectation gets stronger the more frequently it is repeated.

This process works equally well with positive expectations, as those who are positive realise, but it is very difficult to convince those who are not that this is the case, or that people unconsciously act in such a way as to reinforce their expectations. However, by becoming aware of these tendencies, people can realise that they have a choice in attitude or outlook – the way they view issues – and effect change.

Nevertheless there are those who make little progress. They may rationalise this, claiming that they could have found treasure if it had not been under water, which they fear or dislike, but in a castle, for instance. Their insistence upon the 'reality' of the water prevents them acknowledging what it represents and that their inability to overcome it at fantasy level indicates a defence against the unknown and, more specifically, against the unknown aspects of themselves. Indeed, some will acknowledge that this is the case and that they don't want to look into themselves too closely, either out of fear of what they may find, or because of the implications it will have for their lives. Certainly it is important to recognise that there are many people who will hold on to their problems, including potentially life-threatening illnesses, rather than take responsibility for change. Bernie Siegel, a noted surgeon and Assistant Clinical Professor of Surgery at Yale Medical School, estimates that, when given a choice between surgery for serious illness and a change in lifestyle, 80 per cent will opt for the former, because it demands no action on their part, transfers responsibility elsewhere, and maintains the status quo.

Frequently people make the excuse that they 'got nowhere' with the exercise because they 'drifted off' or 'fell asleep'. Rather like illness, sleep is all too often an excuse for inactivity and a way of excusing responsibility for tasks the person doesn't wish to perform. It is therefore a classic way of avoiding one's potentials, along with the responsibilities and fears which attach to them. Domestic and zoo animals frequently curl up and sleep when stressed in some way, presumably on the principle that if they lie quietly or play 'doggo' the threat will go away. Humans react similarly when their cages are rattled. However, as John le Carré has observed, 'By changing nothing we hang on to what we understand, even if it is the bars of our own gaol' (*The Russia House*, p.122). Therefore, being 'rattled' occasionally can be liberating, and so psychological approaches to healing address a person's fears in ways which are examined in the following chapter.

6

CULTIVATING HEALTHY ATTITUDES

Keep your face always towards the sunshine and the shadows will fall behind you.
Walt Whitman

The psychologist William James described the self-actualiser as the person who knows the different parts of himself and can live freely and without fear. However, Freud recognised that most people fear knowledge of themselves, their impulses and emotions, and that this is a major cause of psychological illness. Maslow shared this view, observing that man tends to avoid any knowledge that could give rise to self-dislike or feelings of inferiority, inadequacy, weakness and shame, indeed anything that might confirm has worst suspicions about himself, and that he avoids these unpleasant or dangerous truths by repression and other defences. Fear therefore serves as a defence or protection of self-image, self-esteem and self-respect.

However, Maslow perceived that it is only his darker side that man avoids, but also his better side: his talents, potentialities, capacities and destiny. The previous exercise frequently highlights those fears and anxieties which prevent people discovering, developing or utilising their talents and potentials. Indeed the power object, the pendant, is introduced simply because a very significant proportion of those who attempt the exercise are otherwise unable to overcome their fears sufficiently to complete it.

On the face of it, this reaction seems quite paradoxical inasmuch as people might be expected to rejoice in the discovery of their talents and strive to make the most of them. However, in the Western tradition those such as Prometheus, Oedipus, Adam and Eve, who defied the gods by seeking out their secrets, were punished heavily for their arrogance and were held up as examples to others not to be god-like. In the Christian tradition Adam and his descendants – the entire human race – were punished by the Fall from God's favour and consequent loss of Paradise. Within Christianity, therefore, God is the supreme force, and man utterly powerless. The projection of all human powers into God results not only in man's separation from his potentials and alienation from himself, but also in a tendency towards slavish dependence on external forces and the view that self-assertion is bad and sinful. The discovery of personal potentials and talents may therefore bring exhilaration, but also fear of their dangers and responsibilities, and thus conflict and confusion.

Defences against fear

Maslow points to the many talented women who adopt a defensive attitude of pseudo-stupidity because their intellectual ability compromises their image of themselves and others' view of them as truly feminine, especially if the males in their lives are threatened by it. He observes that timid men may also view their intellectual strengths as likely to evoke the hostility of others who perceive them as a challenge, and so keep them well concealed.

However, a person's defences may be so subtle that unless his anxieties and fears overwhelm him altogether he is able to repress them and to deny even to himself that they exist. Frequently, therefore, people do not know they are afraid. However, to such a person the unfamiliar, the vaguely perceived, the mysterious, hidden or unexpected are all likely to be threatening. One way of rendering these things familiar, predictable, manageable and controllable, and thus non-frightening and harmless, is to know and understand them. Knowledge itself may therefore have an anxiety-reducing function. Indeed it is well-established that scientists typically have a lower tolerance of ambiguity and uncertainty than non-scientists. Over-attachment to rationality, logic and reason is a common defence against the unknown, and the reason why some people are frightened of relinquishing conscious control even slightly, and find relaxation and imagery very difficult.

However, just as seeking knowledge may be a means of reducing anxiety, avoiding it can be also. Maslow suggests that it was safer for the Germans living near the Dachau concentration camp not to know what was happening there and to 'turn a blind eye', because this meant they did not have to do anything about it, and thus put themselves at risk, or live with the knowledge of their cowardice. Similarly, it is easier to turn a deaf ear to the screams and cries of a neighbour's child, because to discover it is being neglected or abused requires us to act, or to live with the knowledge of our failure to do so. Not knowing, or ignorance, is often a defence against taking responsibility and action.

The threat of action

Action is threatening because it involves change, which brings uncertainty and creates instability. Therefore it is resisted in favour of the familiar and habitual, which provide a sense of security and identity, however frail. Rigidity of thinking, attitude and behaviour, like lack of curiosity, many so-called learning difficulties and pseudo-stupidity, are defences, which by confining people to the familiar prevent them confronting change, and thus their fear.

Change is an intrinsic feature of existence, however, and to resist it is a defence against life itself. Unsurprisingly, therefore, those who do so typically live restricted, confined, 'small' lives. This restriction to the known and the safe means that to a great extent such people do not know what they fear because they never allow themselves to encounter it. One might reasonably conclude that what they fear is fear itself and that they tend to avoid those situations in which they expect to find it, even if the expectation is unjustified. Accordingly the scope of their lives is largely determined by the nature of their expectations or beliefs, and this has enormous implications for health and illness.

Expectation effects

It has been found that expectation influences blood levels of
hormones that are important in activating the body's immune
system. Positive and negative expectations appear to have
opposite effects, respectively enhancing or depressing the
immune response. This comes as little suprise to those
familiar with traditional approaches to healing whose practitioners not infrequently achieve dramatic or miracle cures by
instilling positive expectation in their patients or reversing
the negative expectation engendered by spells or hexes.
Arguably modern physicians often do likewise, albeit rather
less explicitly than in the case described by Larry Dossey
where a contemporary US doctor successfully pitted his
medicine against that of an adversary by conducting a
dehexing ceremony. Such operations are hardly commonplace in modern Western society (as opposed to other parts
of the world where they are), but the importance of
expectation or belief is well established in orthodox medicine, where doctors frequently prescribe a placebo or
imitation medicine. Although its effects have been recognised
for centuries, it is only relatively recently that the placebo has
received serious attention from medical researchers.

Although it is not understood how, it is now accepted that
the placebo can have more profound effects on organic
illness, including allegedly incurable malignancies, than
drugs. It seems that the placebo works solely because the
person expects it to. Nevertheless it is doubtful whether the
placebo, or any other treatment for that matter, would prove
effective without the person's will to live, that is, their
positive attitude towards recovery.

The importance of the protection conferred by a positive
approach to life is increasingly being acknowledged. Attitude
is now recognised as an important indicator of who
succumbs to illness and who does not. Early this century
William James observed that the sanguine and the healthy-
minded live habitually on the sunny side of the misery line,
while the depressed and melancholy live beyond it in
darkness and apprehension. The link between psychological
factors and the development of illness has also long been

CULTIVATING HEALTHY ATTITUDES

recognised. Throughout history physicians have observed that cancer occurs more commonly among those of melancholic disposition than in the more sanguine, and those who succumb to cancer have been found to be characterised by negative attitudes and the tendency to helplessness and despair. Studies have shown that the personality profiles of students who eventually succumb to cancer are almost identical with those who later commit suicide (Siegel, 1990). Typically they are restricted in their expression of emotions, especially aggression, and of their needs. They also tend to report more stress. Indeed, psychological factors are now known to be of considerable importance in determining whether or not a person experiences stress.

Stress depends to a great extent on an individual's attitude towards and interpretation of events; on whether they appraise them as a threat or a challenge, as positive or negative. Those who tend to view circumstances positively will see them as opportunities to learn, grow and develop, and will not only cope with them but thrive in consequence.

Those who view circumstances negatively will tend to see them as adverse or stressful, and their focus on the negative will preclude them seeing events in any other way. This accent on negative outcomes frequently obscures the possibilities in a situation for self-development, achievement, fulfilment of potentials and satisfaction of needs. This difference in attitude can be vitally important, quite literally, in that it may determine not only people's susceptibility to illness but also their prospects of survival.

Studies have shown a correlation between mental attitude and length of survival among cancer patients, those whose cancer spontaneously remits being more positive in attitude than those whose cancer develops. Similarly, cancer patients who outlive predicted life expectancies typically refuse to give up in the face of stress and are more flexible and willing to make changes. Heart patients who are anxious, fearful and negative in outlook are also found to be less likely to survive than those who are calm and positive.

Flexibility of attitude emerges as a particularly crucial factor in recovery, those responding poorly to treatment being characterised by rigidity and the tendency to hold on

109

to their self-image and the familiar. Successful treatment of illness thus involves relaxation of mental attitudes, beliefs, negative emotions and expectations. Indeed, the benefits of physical relaxation can only be derived when this is achieved, and are greater when positive expectation is instilled.

Cultivating healthy attitudes

Recognition of the importance of positive attitudes and expectations has led to the idea that positive emotions are not only life-enhancing but life-giving experiences which, in themselves, constitute healing. What is sometimes referred to as attitudinal healing thus focuses on creating attitude change by transforming fears and negative expectations into positive emotions and attitudes. Increasingly humour and laughter are being seen as valuable in overcoming negative attitudes and emotions.

The distinguished ethologist, Konrad Lorenz, once observed that 'we don't take humour seriously enough', and until relatively recently this was certainly true of orthodox medicine and science. However, the psychological and physiological benefits of laughter have long been recognised. In Eastern traditions the Buddha, who sees the cosmic 'joke' or truth of the whole universe, laughs, and thus personifies the Eastern belief in the healing power of laughter. Accordingly laughter is seen as 'wholesome' – making the person whole.

Similarly, in the Bible it is stated that a merry heart works like a doctor, and some 400 years ago mirth was described as 'sufficient cure in itself'. More recently the idea of mirth as medicine was highlighted by Norman Cousins, who attributed his own recovery from an 'incurable' condition to the healing power of laughter. Support for his claims have been provided by research which suggests that laughter stimulates catecholamines which in turn trigger the release of endorphins, the body's natural pain-killers, thereby promoting a sense of well-being and relaxation, and blocking the sensation of pain. Laughter has also been found to benefit heart and lung function, relaxing the diaphragm, exercising the lungs, increasing blood oxygen levels and toning the entire cardio-vascular system.

As we laugh, breathing becomes more spasmodic and deep, and heart rate, muscle tension and blood pressure increase, but as laughter subsides there is a drop in these functions, which leaves the body relaxed. Humour may therefore relieve pain by physiological means but also indirectly by diverting attention away from it. The increasing understanding of the role of laughter in promoting well-being has led to the formation of the 'Nurses for Laughter' group at Oregon Health Sciences University, the members of which wear badges with the logo 'Warning – humour may be hazardous to your illness', and a humour room has recently been opened at the St Joseph's Hospital's Stehlin Foundation for Cancer Research, Houston.

The ability to see the lighter side of life is now being widely claimed as advantageous in the prevention and cure of illness, in increasing chances of survival and improving the quality of life of those who are seriously ill, and is being promoted in psychological approaches to healing.

In practice doctors generally ignore these psychological factors totally and often programme patients with negative rather than positive expectations, giving gloomy prognoses and little hope of recovery. Three-quarters of the side-effects of radio- and chemotherapy result from the beliefs of patients fostered by the negative suggestions of physicians. This, in Siegel's opinion, is why a quarter of all patients receiving chemotherapy start to vomit *before* their treatment. Conventional medical approaches therefore tend to increase the likelihood of stress, rather than reduce it, and to generate fear and anxiety. However, psychological methods are being introduced in dental medicine in order to attract anxious patients with negative attitudes and expectations back to the dentist, and to instil positive expectations and health attitudes in children. Nevertheless, health is not the only objective of psychological approaches. Of perhaps greater importance is helping people to live without fear, to be at peace with life and ultimately with death. They are therefore widely used in improving the quality of life of the terminally ill and dying, helping them to complete unfinished business and live their remaining life to the full without fear and guilt.

These ends are achieved in a number of ways. William James recognised, as did generations of healers before him, that problems and potentials go together and that by working through unconscious fears and difficulties potentials can be reached, creativity and solutions springing from areas beyond the rational and everyday mind. These unconscious depths can be accessed primarily through a combination of relaxation and imagery that is directed to confronting fears rather than avoiding them. When thus confronted, fears are often considerably less than anticipated and may be overcome or managed effectively. One valuable application of this approach is in the area of skilled activity, especially sport, where mental rehearsal of an activity and its effects can be used to raise performance. The benefits of imagery in overcoming competitors' anxieties and self-doubts and in training them to perform automatically are well attested and widely promoted by sports psychologists. Similarly, imaginary exercises and role playing are a major feature of assertiveness and social-skills training, which are directed to overcoming fears and uncertainties.

The following exercise uses imagery as a means of accessing and exploring fears and anxieties. It can also be used to confront other unconscious issues, and therefore has a wide range of applications.

Exercise 6
Accessing fears and anxiety through imagery

Take some time to relax in whatever way is most effective for you, allowing your mental and physical tensions to disappear progressively.

Imagine yourself walking into a building. You are carrying a light-sabre – a laser-type sword – which has remarkable powers and gives you complete protection. As you walk through the building you come to a corridor. On the right side of the corridor there are a number of doors. Each is labelled in some way, indicating what lies behind it, and as you pause to read these labels you realise that they represent your fears and anxieties.

Be aware of your feelings as you realise this, and also of any tendency to censor or change the labels. Do not consciously influence or modify the labels in any way. Simply allow them to emerge unconsciously. When you have noted the labels on each door, return to the door bearing the most intriguing or meaningful label. Be aware of your feelings as you stand at the door, and then open the door and enter, using the light-sabre if necessary, either to enter or to protect yourself. If you feel the need for protection, surround yourself in a cone of white light by swirling the sabre above and around you. Upon entering the room, see, feel and be aware of whatever you find, and remain there until you have identified any feelings that arise.

Then, using the light-sabre, illuminate the entire room, so that you can see features that may not have been visible previously. When nothing new emerges flood the area with white light, erasing the contents of the room. Then leave and explore the other rooms in the same way. Having done so, take some time to record your experience.

As indicated previously, this exercise can be used to explore other unconscious features. It can also be used to resolve known conflicts, problems and difficulties by consciously labelling doors on the left side of the corridor.

Commentary

As most people wish to avoid their fears or anxieties this exercise is often difficult or uncomfortable. Some people will not attempt it, while others ostensibly do so but then claim to have fallen asleep, 'drifted off' or 'blanked out'. Some consciously control the exercise, or censor what they find there, often because it seems strange, illogical or unexpected.

One woman entered a door bearing the label *'petits pois'* and found a room full of vegetables, which she found difficult to take seriously because they seemed both harmless and meaningless. Her only other impression of them was that they related in some way to her job as a teacher. Prompted by the somewhat cynical remark of a group member, she admitted later to being 'fed up' with 'vegetables' – her description of the very low ability children she taught – and to her fear that she was becoming one in the process.

Some people find that they are able to discern a label on a door only after they have entered a room, but not one that the contents would appear to justify, suggesting that the true

113

nature of their fears is not known to them. A good example of this came from a young woman who, on entering an unidentified door, found the body of her two-year-old cousin lying in a coffin. In real life this unfortunate child had been murdered by his father. The image might therefore reasonably be taken as suggestive of a fear of death or violence. However, when asked how she would label the door the woman immediately said 'Betrayed trust', and she subsequently acknowledged that the father's betrayal of the child's and others' trust in him had led her to doubt all men. As a result, the relationship with her partner had gone sour and she recognised that unless she could heal the hurt resulting from the child's death it would destroy her prospects of the marriage and children she desired.

The process of labelling can thus be very significant. Having examined the label, many people anticipate the contents of the rooms before they enter, revealing the nature of their expectations. For some the anxiety and panic generated prevents them entering the room at all, showing the power of their negative expectations and their limiting effects upon action, even within fantasy.

Some people will not make use of their light-sabre to enter the rooms, suggesting a failure to make the best of their opportunities and thus to grow and develop.

Attitudes to the light-sabre are generally interesting. Unlike the diamond pendant which many people tend to reject or devalue because of essentially sexist associations, everyone seems willing to accept it, men and women alike, but some then forget they have it. This may be a rationalisation that enables them to avoid their fears, or may reveal their tendency to repress potentials and other positive attributes that would help them to cope in a given situation. The tendency to overlook their strengths may be a significant feature in how they deal with their anxieties and fears. Others simply don't trust the light-sabre, betraying their tendency to doubt and negativity.

The ease or difficulty of access to the rooms is also an interesting feature of this exercise, suggesting how deeply or otherwise fears and anxieties are hidden and how impenetrably. Those who tend to be highly anxious or panicky may find their doors wide open or ajar, while others find theirs locked, bolted, jammed or sealed. The former often live with a constant dread of their worst fears being realised and show marked avoidance tendencies and 'flight' responses. The latter typically show and experience much less anxiety, unless or until they are required to confront well-concealed fears. Thus, although manifestly less anxious, these people may be profoundly fearful. Women, although ostensibly more fearful than men, are generally more willing to acknowledge their fears. By comparison, men wish to avoid being seen as fearful. They therefore tend not to admit to their fears, and find ways of avoiding them and of not doing the exercise. Avoidance strategies therefore tend to reflect cultural differences between the sexes.

One person found a double door – the outer one opening outwards and the inner one opening inwards across a narrow corridor – suggestive of high security. Others find that they enter the room using the door as a shield or barrier, and those who feel inclined to do so are often alarmed when the door opens outwards towards them, denying them this protection. Many are amazed by the thickness of the door and its strength, some doors being fortified like castles, others being steel doors of the kind found in some prisons or on ships. Some find they can gain access to the room only by using the special powers of the light-sabre, which suggests that ordinarily these areas would be inaccessible to them.

Of those who do enter the rooms, many are surprised to find that they are quite different to what they expected, and frequently are not particularly threatening. One person, a teacher, upon entering a classroom during a maths lesson, could not understand how this everyday situation represented 'fear', which was the label clearly printed on the door. Returning later to the room out of sheer curiosity he imagined sitting down at a desk at the back of the class. As he did so he felt an overwhelming sense of anxiety, and a desire to hide and not be 'picked on' by the teacher. However, the teacher did summon him to the front of the class and directed him to complete a mathematical formula written on the blackboard. Being unable to do so because he had missed the first part of the lesson, the man experienced terror at the prospect of 'making a fool of himself' – a major concern throughout his life, which he was subsequently able to work through and resolve. This fear of incompetence is very common in men, who are conditioned to achieve.

Another man found himself drawn to a door labelled 'garden', which surprised him as he took great pleasure in gardens and gardening. However, on entering the garden via the door he was very disappointed. Instead of a lush, colourful, exotic garden of the kind he expected, he found himself in very dull and colourless surroundings. He later described the trees as 'very ordinary English trees', the landscape as flat and uninteresting and without pools, streams, springs or flowers. Although profoundly disappointed by this he was unable to see how it related to his fears. When asked about the possible significance of the garden and his reference to 'English' trees in particular, he explained that he had felt very unsettled since leaving his former employment three years previously, as it had taken him abroad and to the tropics, where he relished the heat and the jungle. He and his wife were planning to leave Britain to live in a better climate where they could spend more time outdoors in their garden. He realised that his imagery may be an indication of his unconscious fears about the success of this venture and the possibility of disappointment.

For another man a room labelled 'parties' highlighted his difficulties in relating to and being in close proximity with other people.

The imagery of others may be more dramatic but just as symbolic. Thus some find their rooms full of water or ruins, open to the elements or without any floors, suggesting exposure or lack of security. Some find the contents of certain rooms are obscured, covered in dust-sheets that can't be removed, or otherwise concealed, indicating a reluctance to confront them; this is frequently indicated in the emotional reactions to these hidden issues, which are invariably disproportionate to their overt features. However, having examined the room and erased its contents, many people like it and feel reluctant to leave. In some cases they may decide against erasing the contents as they realise this is unnecessary. One woman, entering a room labelled 'paranoia' and expecting to find in it people or things attacking her, was surprised to find black lines of force emanating from her to other people whose backs were turned to her. She also saw a spider scuttling across the floor and felt a desire to stamp on it, which she would never do in reality. She therefore spoke to it and asked it what it was doing, and it said it had been startled by her entering the room and was running away from her. She realised that, rather than being attacked by others, she was in fact projecting her own negativity onto them. She therefore erased the lines but left the spider to go about its business, to the relief of both of them.

Many of those who complete the exercise are surprised to find that they feel comfortable with their fears and are able to deal with them easily and adequately. In some cases their fears have been unjustified. For others it enables a greater understanding and exploration of their fears and their ways of dealing with them. These approaches have therefore been widely used in confronting issues such as death, helping people explore their feelings about their own death and that of others.

A fear shared by both sexes is of being thought 'childish' or 'silly'. This fear relates not merely to the content of a person's imagery, but to the process of imagination itself, some people being reluctant to engage in it or admit to doing so, and others adopting cynical, sceptical or dismissive attitudes towards it. The limiting effect this may have on a person's experience was highlighted for me during a professional training course quite unrelated to healing. One woman, who was clearly reluctant to engage in an exercise, told me that she would feel happier about it if I had not suggested that the group members 'play about' with a certain idea. She felt that by so doing I was trivialising the issue, and effectively asking group members to waste time. Being rather surprised by her reaction, I asked her to elaborate more on her understanding of the concept 'play', and it became clear that to her it was quite incompatible with 'work' and not to be treated seriously. I pointed out to her that play is the means by which young humans and animals learn about their environment and themselves, and as such is crucial to cognitive development. Play deprivation impairs intellectual development and functioning, so rather than being in any sense wasteful, play is highly productive and creative. Reassured that I was not 'belittling' the enterprise we were jointly engaged in, she consented to continue with it.

Given what is now known about the physiology of laughter, its beneficial effects on health and the undesirable health consequences of psychological rigidity, I found this suppression of fun and playfulness somewhat alarming, the more so because the concern not to be 'childish' suggests a rather tenuous self-identity and maturity.

Concern about the 'childishness' or 'silliness' of imagery exercises sometimes prompts the question of their applicability to children.

Research has shown that children who are imaginative tend to score more highly on tests of intellectual ability and are better able to cope than children who are unimaginative, and that encouraging imagination and also creativity and self-expression improves the ability to cope and learn (Oaklander, 1978). It is for this reason that play and all kinds of imaginary activities, including visualisation and guided fantasy, are increasingly being used by teachers at all educational levels. Imagery is also being used increasingly in therapy, not only with those who have learning difficulties but also with those who are emotionally disturbed. Violet Oaklander, in *Windows to Our Children*, a book on the therapeutic uses of imagery in working with children, explains that 'usually a child's fantasy process is the same as their life process. We can look into the inner realms of the child's being through fantasy. We can bring out what is kept hidden or avoided and we can also find out what's going on in the child's life, from her perspective.'

Ways of doing so include using guided fantasy, but also all forms of story-telling, talking, writing, painting, drawing, modelling, poetry and puppetry. Oaklander observes that simply by drawing a picture of a fantasy and writing a summary statement on it, children may indicate very succinctly where they are in their lives, and their feelings about it. This approach is therefore used to access children's feelings and to enable them to become aware of themselves and their existence in the world. It is particularly appropriate in dealing with stress, trauma, phobias and issues that children have difficulty expressing. However, Brian Roet (1988) advocates the use of imagery as a means whereby parents can gain insight into the normally hidden realms of their children's experience – their fears, anxieties, needs, wishes and preoccupations – and thus monitor emotional and psychological development more sensitively.

7

INFLUENCING THE HEALING PROCESS

Fantasy is the servant of reality.
J.O. Stevens

The exercise in the previous chapter often demonstrates the way that imagination produces real physical effects such as sweating, trembling, 'goose-flesh', palpitations, increased heart rate and respiration, dry mouth, tightness of the throat and other muscle tensions, which are experienced as anxiety or panic. There is nothing new in this awareness. All traditional approaches to healing tacitly acknowledge the influence of imagery on physiological and emotional functions, 'imaginative medicine' being the oldest and most widely used system of healing throughout the world. For shamans who have little or no direct knowledge of anatomy or physiology, images are as much a physiological reality as any other body function, capable both of producing symptoms of disease and curing them. Accordingly, since the earliest of times, they have worked indirectly on the body through the creation of powerful imagery.

Some four hundred years ago the French writer Montaigne described the effects of imagery, declaring that 'a powerful imagination begets the thing itself', often producing illness and even death (Trechman, undated). He related many cases in support of his claim, including that of a woman who became ill and died after a practical joker told her that she had eaten 'cat pasty'. Montaigne recognised that the same principle could be used just as effectively in treatment, and described various cures attributable to it. He therefore drew attention to the placebo effect several hundred years before it received serious attention within orthodox medicine.

Nowadays the curative possibilities of the imagination are acknowledged, although not fully understood, as are its potentially lethal outcomes in response to hexes, curses and precipitous and ill-judged medical prognoses. Awareness that intense imagery can produce quite definite physiological effects, and may result in death, has led some doctors to warn against the widespread medical practice of pronouncing life expectancies. It now seems clear that when a doctor 'gives' a patient six months to live, he takes away much more, not only time as such, but also hope and positive expectation. Left to imagine 'the worst', most patients do, and effectively ensure its occurrence. Indeed, there is a very real sense in which imagination *is* creativity.

Imagination as creativity

It can easily be demonstrated that saliva production may be increased by imagining sucking a lemon, and that the thought of finger-nails scraping across a blackboard, or a tin plate being scratched with a metal fork, is sufficient to produce quite definite physical reactions. Studies have revealed that it is possible to increase heart rate by imagining oneself running, alter pupil size by changing the distance at which features are perceived 'in the mind's eye', and increase muscle tension by imagining lifting progressively heavier weights (Jacobsen, 1929; Lichstein and Lipshitz, 1982; Shaw, 1946). Dramatic physiological effects also accompany intense sexual or phobic imagery. Unpleasant imagery or memory images of negative or unhappy experiences can produce changes in heart rate and other cardiovascular functions, skin resistance and muscle tension. Imagery may also elicit changes in blood sugar and blood hormone levels, gastro-intestinal activity, and the immune system.

Imagining pleasant, non-threatening experiences may slow heart and respiratory rate, lower blood pressure, improve immune functioning and reduce muscle tension. Indeed, it is now clear from extensive research that imagery has effects on the body which in many instances are as real as those produced by drugs. Accordingly imagery may be regarded as a potent therapeutic agent, or medicine.

Exactly how imagery achieves its effects remains unclear. It may be thought that the content of imagery is crucial to the changes that occur in the body, and so imagining lying under a warm sun may promote the sensation of warmth. This is not necessarily the case, however. It is possible to increase the temperature of the hands quite effectively while imagining them submerged in icy water. This may be because absorption in imagery promotes relaxation, a physiological feature of which is warmth resulting from the vasodilation of blood vessels. Nevertheless, the content of imagery is generally a significant determinant of its physical effects. Research suggests that the internal processes are much the same whether an object or situation is actually perceived or merely imagined, and that images generate similar, albeit not necessarily identical, internal responses to the actual stimuli themselves. Thus, for instance, during visual imagery the visual cortex of the brain is normally activated, although the more peripheral visual pathways such as the pupil may or may not be involved. Imagery therefore seems to be an analogue, or parallel, process which has a one-to-one correspondence with the physical processes it represents.

The existence of a vast network of neural connections between the right hemisphere of the brain and the limbic system, that area primarily concerned with emotion and fundamental physiological processes and now thought to be centrally concerned with the processing of imagery, offers a possible explanation for the implication of imagery in emotional and other physiological functions. Right-brain processes affect emotional and related physiological functions directly, and, to the extent that they remain non-verbal, these are to a great extent unconscious and apparently involuntary. Imagery appears to serve as a medium or transformer whereby these processes become conscious or verbalisable, and the limbic system is the area in which this occurs. However, as is the case with any 'bridge' or 'border' area, it can, in principle at least, be used in two directions – in this case, to translate verbal left-brain messages into non-verbal imaginal terminology which can be processed by the right brain.

On the face of it these translations from right to left and from left to right may appear to be equivalent processes, but closer examination suggests that they are not. The translation of unconscious, pre-verbal, right-brain messages into left-brain terminology effectively involves 'giving voice' to them. It has been noted in chapter 3 that in certain circumstances where this translation process is impaired right-brain messages may continue to affect emotional and physiological processes without rational interpretation. In such cases people have no words for their feelings and thus no way of expressing them other than physically.

However, the translation process from left brain to right can be likened to a kind of shouting into the dark. The conscious, verbal, left-brain message may well be received and acted on, but there is no way of knowing this because the non-verbal, right-brain processes have no 'say in the matter' – no voice with which to reply – and unless the individual concerned is insightful, or actively looking for signs that the message has been received, he or she may remain unaware of any response and assume that it has not been effected. In such circumstances, people may be unaware that feelings or thoughts they have voiced are being expressed physically, and attribute physiological effects to involuntary processes beyond their control. Whereas Alixythymia – having no voice for feelings – is relatively uncommon, having little insight into the effects of voicing feelings in physical terms appears to be very common indeed. People frequently express themselves, and especially their reactions to stressors, in physical imagery, apparently unaware that in so doing they may be influencing physical and emotional processes, and thus determining their characteristic physical and emotional reactions to stress. A correspondence between a person's use of physical metaphors or figures of speech and their characteristic stress reactions, physical illnesses and symptoms can often be observed, and frequently *is* by patients who make these connections only after developing an illness. It is not unusual for breast cancer patients to admit that they have needed to 'get something off their chest' or have tended to 'let things get on their tits', or those with bowel disorders to describe themselves as 'full of shit', or always 'taking other people's shit'.

These characteristic figures of speech appear to be a fairly reliable indicator of actual or likely health problems, although there is as yet no firm empirical evidence to support such a conclusion. However, Franz Alexander, a pioneer of psychosomatic medicine, has indicated that there is evidence to suggest that certain emotional conflicts possess specificities and accordingly tend to afflict certain internal organs, just as certain pathological micro-organisms are known to have a special affinity for certain organs. These 'target organs', or parts of the body with special significance to the conflicts in a person's life, are therefore the most likely areas for disease to take root. The surgeon Bernie Siegel is convinced that individuals sensitise these target organs quite unconsciously through their use of verbal imagery. Accordingly the mind affects the body's tissues without any conscious awareness on the part of the individual concerned. Therefore, he argues, those who typically insist that they will succeed 'if it kills them', may find it does. Other typical phrases are:

It . . .
gets on my nerves, tits, wick, up my nose, under my skin, irritates me;
gets me going, on the hop, on the run, moves me;
gives me the hots, the runs, the jitters, the creeps, the screaming abdabs, the hump;
winds me up, ties me in knots, screws me up, turns my gut;
pisses me off;
puts my back up;
beats me, kills me, pains me, grieves me, sickens me;
sets my teeth on edge, leaves a nasty taste in my mouth;
drives me mad, hairless;
breaks my heart, sticks in my throat;
sours me off, hacks me off, chokes me;
makes my skin creep, crawl, my hair stand on end;
makes me sick (often to death), seethe, go hot, cold, hot and cold, uptight;

makes me want to throw up, vent my spleen, burst, erupt;
bores me stiff, rigid;
is a pain in the neck, head, backside;
is a grind;
is eating me alive.

Nevertheless, and despite being on the blink, shattered, knackered, wasted, worn out, cut up, destroyed, wrecked, totally fed up, sick with worry and dying for a change, people don't bat an eyelid, shrug it off, turn a blind eye or a deaf ear, grin and bear it – often because they haven't 'got the guts' to do otherwise.

Irrespective of any connection these phrases may have with physical symptoms and illness, research suggests that images do relate to physiological states, and may precede or follow physiological changes, indicating both a causative and a reactive role (Achterberg, 1985). Images can be induced by conscious, deliberate behaviours and also by unconscious acts, such as reverie and dreaming, and may be considered as a hypothetical bridge between conscious or unconscious processing and physiological change. They may influence the voluntary or peripheral nervous system, and autonomic functions. Imagery therefore has both direct and indirect effects on the body, not only the musculo-skeletal system, but also the involuntary nervous system, and is in turn effected by these reactions.

In addition imagery has a number of psychological functions. It promotes absorption and a shift in the time sense, which enables relaxation of mental attitudes, beliefs, preoccupations and expectations; provides an alternative mode for representation of issues; is a means of accessing information relevant to unconscious processes; and makes it possible for us consciously to influence psychological and emotional processes of which we are normally unaware.

From a practical point of view imagery has numerous implications for health. By promoting relaxation, both mental and physical, it can reduce stress and its effects, and help ameliorate and steady body functions. It can also provide new perspectives on and insights into emotional and

125

psychological factors relevant to health and illness, and clues to emotional and physical functions which are of value in diagnosis and treatment. It may also be used to influence these processes consciously, in either support of treatment or prevention of disease. Imagery can thus be conceived as a mediator between different worlds of experience. This awareness has formed the basis of shamanic healing practices since the earliest times but, within the field of orthodox Western medicine, has been recognised and applied only relatively recently as a result of the pioneering work of cancer specialist Carl Simonton and his former wife, psychotherapist Stephanie Matthews-Simonton (now Stephanie Simonton-Atchley).

The Simontons recognised two important factors in the etiology of cancer: the effect of stress in depressing the body's immune system, and the influence of a person's beliefs and emotional responses – although not necessarily in this order, as the following extract from their best-selling book *Getting Well Again* makes clear:

> It is our central premise that an illness is not purely a physical problem but rather a problem of the whole person, that it includes not only body but mind and emotions. We believe that emotional and mental states play a significant role both in *susceptibility* to disease, including cancer, and in *recovery* from all disease. We believe that cancer is often an indication of problems elsewhere in an individual's life, problems aggravated or compounded by a series of stresses six to eighteen months prior to the onset of cancer. The cancer patient has typically responded to these problems and stresses with a deep sense of hopelessness, or 'giving up'. This emotional response, we believe, in turn triggers a set of physiological responses that suppress the body's natural defenses and make it susceptible to producing abnormal cells.

Accordingly, they suggest, the first step in getting well is to understand how psychological factors have contributed to illness, and to find ways of influencing them in support of treatment. Both issues, they believe, can be dealt with through a combination of relaxation and mental imagery. They recognise that in helping promote and enhance relaxa-

126

tion, imagery has an important role in decreasing tension and effecting positive physiological changes, including improvement of immune function, and thus in influencing the course of malignancy. Moreover it may be used as a means whereby patients can confront their fears and feelings of hopelessness and helplessness, enabling them to gain a sense of control and a change in attitude; and also as a means to communicate with their unconscious minds, where beliefs antithetical to health may be hidden, and which may yield valuable insights into their condition.

The Simontons therefore developed a method in which patients are instructed to relax three times daily for periods of about twenty minutes while imagining their cancer being destroyed and disposed of by their body's immune system. Patients are first taught a simple form of relaxation which focuses on breathing, and are instructed to repeat silently the word 'relax' and to let go of tensions in various muscle groups of the body. Having achieved relaxation they are asked to imagine their cancer as shrinking or otherwise responding in a positive way to treatment, and are also encouraged to deal with pain in the same way.

Of 159 patients with a diagnosis of medically incurable malignancy treated by the Simontons over a four-year period prior to 1978, none of whom were expected to live more than a year, 22.2 per cent made a full recovery, the disease regressed in a further 19 per cent and stabilised in 27 per cent. There was further tumour growth in 31 per cent of the patients, but average survival time increased by a factor of 2 to 2½. Those who eventually succumbed to the malignancy maintained higher than usual levels of activity and achieved a significant improvement in their quality of life. Abundant anecdotal evidence appears to confirm the Simontons' claim that relaxation and imagery have an important role to play in the treatment of cancer as adjuncts to orthodox medical treatment. Support for their claims also comes from other research which suggests that where psychological methods are employed survival time is two to three times longer than would be predicted on the basis of national norms. After five years, 51 per cent of the patients who had been treated with psychological approaches were still living, compared with only 16 per cent of those who had not received this treatment. Studies have also shown that relaxation and imagery may considerably reduce nausea and pain in cancer patients, reduce the unpleasant side-effects of chemotherapy, increase its effectiveness, and improve immune functions. Success has also been claimed for the effectiveness of relaxation and imagery in the absence of orthodox medical treatments such as surgery, chemotherapy and radiotherapy (Brohn, 1986), although there is no empirical research evidence in support of this. Studies have demonstrated that relaxation and imagery are effective in the treatment of chronic pain, severe orthopaedic trauma, rheumatoid arthritis, burn injury, alcoholism and stress-related conditions. As a result these methods have found a warm reception among the nursing profession, especially in the USA, where increasingly they are taught as part of nurse training.

The number of doctors using these methods in general practice in the USA is also increasing. Nevertheless, medical opinion remains somewhat divided. Doctors generally agree that the patient's attitude is vitally important to recovery and survival and that it is important to do everything to support those with serious illness. There is some dissension, however, as to whether 'everything' should include psychological methods, lest this imply that they may cure or influence the course of diseases such as cancer. After attending a conference run by the *British Journal of Hospital Medicine*, where the results of a number of studies were presented which suggested that a fighting attitude may affect the life expectancy of those suffering from breast cancer, one doctor observed:

> Even if you can prove that willpower increases the concentration of white blood cells in your blood there is no direct relationship between those white cells and cancer resolution. Cancer immunology is one of the most obscure of medical specialities. The only thing we know less about is how the mind works. Trying to explain one from the standpoint of the other is like trying to shoot fish from a rocking boat (John Collee, 'A doctor writes', *The Observer*, 1 April 1990).

128

Accordingly, the medical profession has been slow in implementing psychological approaches or conducting controlled trials on their effectiveness. Research concerning psychological interventions is still very limited and further controlled clinical studies are needed. In practice most doctors dismiss psychological factors totally. Nevertheless there are some indications, such as the increasing number of relevant papers in respected medical journals, that these approaches are now being given more serious consideration in orthodox British medicine.

Psychological approaches involving relaxation and imagery have been introduced into a number of orthodox cancer treatment programmes, most recently at Hammersmith Hospital, London, where, following studies of the use of such methods at the Bristol Cancer Help Centre, doctors have come around to the view that these methods work and are perfectly compatible with traditional methods of treatment.

The following exercise is based on the kind of approach developed by the Simontons. It is not directed necessarily to cancer or any other illness, but more towards the establishment of communication with and insight into the processes of the body, especially those relevant to the promotion of effective healing.

Exercise 7
Imagining the healing process

Imagine sitting after an enjoyable meal in front of an open fire in a deep, comfortable armchair. You feel pleasantly full and content, warm and comfortable, as you sit watching the flames flickering, noticing their colour and shape. After a while your eyes close and you become aware of the smell and the sounds of the fire. You feel its warmth on your face and body, and as you do so the tensions, aches and pains in both seem to dissolve. As you become progressively more and more relaxed you become aware of any areas of residual tension, pain or discomfort, and you either place your hand, or imagine placing your hand, over the area which most impresses itself upon you. Having done so you imagine a tiny replica of yourself standing on that hand and shrinking smaller and smaller so that it can enter your body through the pores of the skin.

Imagine it descending and commencing a full and thorough

investigation of that area, establishing what is happening, and what is needed there, and recording its impressions as it does so in a notebook or into a tape recorder. Try to avoid imposing biological or anatomical details on the situation, and just allow images and impressions to arise spontaneously. Do not censor them in any way.

You may find it useful to talk to, or otherwise interact with, the various features you encounter, in order to gain as full a picture of the situation as possible.

When you are satisfied that you have conducted a full and thorough investigation and reached an assessment of what is needed, relay this information to your body's healing forces, wherever they are situated, and direct them to deal with it in any way that seems appropriate.

Imagine this in as much detail as possible, noting the locations and appearance of the healing forces and how responsive or otherwise they appear. Then supervise them as they tackle the problem. This may require a planning meeting *in situ*, and may involve a long term strategy. If it can be dealt with immediately then supervise progress, insisting on the highest standards of work and that the site is left clean and tidy on its completion. If the job cannot be dealt with immediately, negotiate a programme of work and agree a time-scale, procedures and so on. When this is agreed leave the healing forces to carry out the work, indicating that you will return to monitor progress. Then return to the surface of the body by any route that suggests itself. Allow yourself to return to normal, and take a few minutes to record your experience.

Commentary

Most people find this exercise quite absorbing and often very amusing. Sometimes they are surprised that the area which presents itself as tense, painful or uncomfortable is not one they might have expected. This in itself can be very significant. One woman found her abdomen to be very tense, despite the fact that her persistent problem was a painful hip. In doing the exercise she discovered that her hip was connected with the muscles of her abdomen, which when contracted through tension, created pain elsewhere, and realised that the treatment she was receiving for the hip 'problem' was actually failing to address the true cause of the complaint. Another lady with a malignant cancer in one part of the body found, to her surprise, that her attention was drawn to a quite different area, where secondary growths were subsequently discovered.

Most people looking inside themselves in this way do not 'see' organs and tissue, although on one occasion a woman imagined herself pushing down between 'bolsters' of fat underneath her skin. They may find quasi-biological features such as thickened tubes, tightened sinews and ligaments, seized-up joints and retained fluid, which they know to be features of their medical condition, but for the most part they tend to encounter very non-anatomical features – the most notable example being a woman who looked inside herself and found a herd of Friesian cows and a fat, woolly calf! She was relieved when, instead of running away, they approached her and were friendly, but while she found this pleasant and reassuring, her conscious mind imposed itself, telling her this was nonsense. She then tried to get a different image, but failing to do so, gave up on the exercise. However, there were many ways in which she could have utilised this imagery – by establishing whether the cows had strayed, or needed releasing, feeding or milking, and whether or not they had adequate pasture or water, for example – and when this was pointed out to her she couldn't wait to 'go back' and explore the imagery further.

Some people imagine their pains and tensions as blockages – walls, masonry or piles of rubble. One woman imagined boys riding motorbikes around the inside of her skull as though on a 'wall of death'. Another, seeing her chest problem as a sooty, dusty underground railway station, sent a team of night-shift workers to clean it. This proved very effective, but a few days later she felt as though there was dust in her throat and realised that unless dealt with this could lead to a fire, as was the case in the King's Cross 'Tube' disaster. Wishing to avoid any inflammation, she sent a maintenance team to remove the fluff, hair and dust from the station elevators, which she directed them to stop for this purpose. Another person with a particularly virulent cancer imagined her chest as a deserted underground station, where rubble on the line was holding back rat-infested water flooding from a burst sewer.

The range of imagery produced in this part of the exercise

is always intriguing and fascinating, and leaves no doubt as to the richness and versatility of the human imagination. However, it is more than matched by that summoned in response to the request to imagine the body's healing forces, which is often worthy of both Steven Spielberg and Monty Python. Little men in white suits and various kinds of helmet, equipped with various machines, hi-tech gadgetry, transportation and weaponry are commonplace; some are in more exotic, media-inspired 'Popemobiles', spaceships, 'Miami Vice'-style power-boats, futuristic fire-engines, or more fantastic 'Star Wars'-type space stations and command modules. The influence of television advertising is discernible in the number of 'Tetley Tea-bag' and 'Homepride Flour' men who appear dressed in hygienic white coveralls ready to streamline, automate and rationalise various physical functions.

These rather less 'macho' but nevertheless stereotypically masculine characters make up workforces variously 'armed' with shovels, picks, hammers, power-drills and hoses, water cannons, vacuum suction devices, haulage, construction or demolition equipment – indeed anything and everything appropriate to the tasks in hand. They have their female counterpart in regiments of 'Mrs Mop'-style cleaning ladies, equipped with buckets, brushes and every conceivable cleaning aid. Between them these workers strive to hammer, chisel, oil and lubricate stiff and seized joints, to release tightened screws and vices, demolish or blast away obstructions and blockages, 'declog' or scour veins and arteries, pump or drain away excess fluid, remove grime, dirt and debris, iron muscles and sinews smooth, and sanitise and fumigate.

Other forces may be at work, such as light, water, sound-waves or lasers, infra-red darts, ants or worker bees, tennis balls with teeth to chew away calcium deposits, soldiers or knights doing battle, Cossacks spearing viruses or malignant cells like kebabs. The invention is endless.

The imagery produced may reveal important insights into the effectiveness of the body's healing processes. In some cases they simply are not up to the task of defending the body against invasion, or of maintaining or restoring health. The lady mentioned previously, whose underground station was flooded with rat-infested water, could find only one railway official on duty when she raised the alarm, and he refused to be of any assistance whatever. His attitude was that she should leave the matter alone, and when pressed to do something about the situation he became argumentative and abusive, giving various excuses as to why he could not intervene and the dangers of doing so. Other people find that their healing forces are indifferent, unresponsive, hostile or 'out to lunch'.

Perhaps not surprisingly the most unresponsive 'forces' are found in those people with immuno-deficiencies and related conditions. One woman with rheumatoid arthritis imagined her immune system as a fire-station where the firemen were all watching television and totally unwilling to respond to her call for assistance. Further investigation revealed that the alarm-bell system was distinctly 'dodgy', the firemen all too fat to slide down their poles, the fire-engines insufficient in number, and those available, like the firemen, in a poor state of maintenance. Another lady with the same condition 'telephoned' a request for assistance to the headquarters of her body's healing force and was rather rudely told that they were busy and to call back in two weeks!

Some people find that their healing forces are willing and responsive but quite disorganised; one man's fire-fighting team set out and travelled throughout his entire body before eventually locating the fire in their own control room. Nevertheless, in many instances the healing forces are highly efficient and well organised – German panzer divisions, closely co-ordinated special-operations task forces, colonies of ants, and so on. Occasionally they may be too efficient and need to be restrained or retrained, as in the case of a woman suffering from a life-threatening auto-immune condition who found her healing forces frantically building quite unnecessary and obstructive bridges in an attempt to provide an effective defence system. However, healing forces may appear to be rather more efficient than they actually are. One woman described hers energetically spraying foam over a virulent weed, but achieving no effect whatsoever. She subsequently realised that the foam being used was a soap completely inadequate for the task, and replaced it with a powerful herbicide.

Sometimes the healing resources are badly depleted and unable to carry out the necessary work adequately or quickly enough, as was the case where a 'force' of just two men were laying the foundations of a vast motorway bridge with the benefit of only a portable cement-mixer, a bucket and two spades.

While this imagery is frequently entertaining and amusing, it does have a very serious aspect and can be quite remarkably powerful in providing insights into bodily functions, health and illness. On a purely physical level many people find that chronic tensions and long-standing pains are relieved or disappear altogether, while other discover previously unrecognised connections between apparently discrete muscle groups and body parts which may have important implications for the management and treatment of certain conditions including referred pain.

The imagery may provide some indication of the status of the individual's immune response, together with clues as to how this may be consciously influenced in support of treatment. It may also reveal unconscious attitudes and expectations relevant to health and illness.

Various negative and unhealthy attitudes may be highlighted. The person referred to previously, who on contacting her healing forces was told to call again in two weeks, simply accepted this response without demur, and many people, notably women, tend to do likewise, reflecting a failure to assert even their most fundamental or vital health needs. This form of self-denial can prove fatal, as can other responses. One woman with a long history of ill-health admitted that she 'couldn't be bothered' trying to gain a positive response from her healing forces. This raised the question of what benefits she derived from illness that made health not worth striving for. Another woman accepted without question the hasty response of her healing-force 'foreman' that the 'job' she had requested was impossible.

Indeed, certain people are only too ready to take 'no' for an answer, possibly because they want others to do for them what they can't do for themselves, and often because they don't actually want to get well. Such defeatism, fatalism or downright complacency are often indications that a person has abdicated all responsibility for his or her health – and as Siegel has observed, fatalism often proves fatal. Resistance of this kind, negative attitudes and expectations, need to be identified in order to prevent them generating negative outcomes.

Many people pay lip-service to self-help and the notion of taking responsibility for their health or recovery while secretly hoping that they won't need to, and will discover something or somebody that will make the effort unnecessary. Some 'go along' with psychological approaches merely to pander to the whims of others, or because they are unable to say 'no' to them. Their efforts are half-hearted and often generate stress and anxiety. Indeed, one of the lessons that advocates of psychological approaches need to learn, and learn well, is that for some people illness and even death is easier and preferable than having to reconstruct their lives in such a way as to achieve and maintain health. Earnest relatives and friends may try to impose what they perceive as life-saving strategies on people who simply want to die in peace, and fail to recognise that in so doing they are imposing their needs on the patient rather than allowing the patient to choose for himself. Some people simply do not realise the enormity of the task faced by those who choose life and health over illness. One elderly lady admitted only after major surgery to remove much of her stomach and bowels that she was 'sick to death' of the life she had led throughout almost fifty years of marriage. During this time she had subjugated her needs to those of her family and a domineering husband, whom she had never 'had the guts' to stand up to. Now that her 'guts' had largely been taken away she doubted her ability to make the changes she needed in her life, and pressure from her daughter to use psychological methods in support of her treatment simply reinforced her view that she was not strong enough to assert herself against the wishes of her family.

Another woman on her deathbed revealed to a still indignant daughter that she had not informed anyone about a growth that subsequently proved inoperable, because it was the only area of choice left to her in a life totally dominated by the needs and wishes of her family. The horrified daughter was informed that her mother had been determined to make just one decision for herself, even if it proved to be her last.

The choice of life and health may also be similarly thwarted by one's 'nearest and dearest'. Many people who, largely as a result of the use of psychological methods, have reappraised their lives and recognised their needs and potentials report difficulties in attempting to fulfil these because of the opposition of others. Recovering patients are therefore often in much the same position as released prisoners or drug addicts who find 'going straight' or effecting positive changes difficult because of the expectations and assumptions of those around them.

While the imagery of some people betrays fundamentally negative attitudes, that of others reflects their positive outlook and determination. One woman who experienced none of the usual side-effects of chemotherapy imagined it as champagne bubbles coursing through her body. Not only did she not find the experience adverse, she actually enjoyed it, much to the astonishment of her medical consultants. Her experience is similar to that reported by eleven-year-old Joanne Gillespie in *Brave Heart*, a personal account of her fight against cancer of the brain. She attributes her complete lack of sickness throughout radiotherapy to visualisation, in which she imagined 'nice things like picnics, holidays and dancing'.

An individual's responses to the imagery he or she produces may also be indicative of important attitudes. Some people are so committed to the idea of being ill that they are reluctant to accept what appear to be positive signs of health. Many people live with the expectation of becoming ill, and negatively programme themselves, not merely for illness, but for specific conditions which have afflicted family members, relatives and work colleagues. If these expectations are challenged they often take the attitude 'well, you have to die of something', apparently oblivious that old age is an option. For too many people illness is viewed as inevitable rather than avoidable, and for some it is a socially acceptable form of suicide, a way out of an unendurable situation.

Others are reassured by their imagery. A woman who had used visualisation as part of her treatment for cancer was initially alarmed when she was no longer able to summon the images which represented her disease, until she realised that this might mean there were no more cancer cells, which was subsequently confirmed by a body scan.

In association with the Simontons, Jeanne Achterberg has drawn up a list of tentative criteria for the evaluation of the content of a person's mental imagery (Achterberg *et al.*, 1977). The representation of cancer cells as ants or eggs in a incubator is regarded as negative, suggesting the likely proliferation of the disease. Similarly, crabs and other crustaceans, which are tough, tenacious and impregnable, are generally taken as symbolising the potency of the disease. Rats are also seen as negative, but this is not necessarily the case because, as one workshop participant pointed out, on the positive side 'there are a hell of a lot of ways to get rid of them'. Nevertheless, rats greedily consuming the piles of chemotherapy treatment is clearly undesirable.

The Simontons recognise that imagery involves a highly personal symbolic language, and that the meaning of any one symbol will vary greatly from one person to another. Thus one person's image of strength and power may well be another's symbol of weakness. For example, the humble mouse is often seen as weak and timid rather than powerful and yet in Hindu mythology it pulls Lord Krishna's chariot and is a very potent symbol. Given such variation it is important to explore an individual's imagery with them, rather than impose meaning onto it. The significance of the imagery may not be immediately apparent and so, in order to translate the beliefs inherent in it, the Simontons consider it necessary for the person to 'try on' the image to discover its meaning. They regard free drawing as a particularly valuable means of exploring imagery and facilitating discussion and understanding.

Notwithstanding individual differences in imagery, the Simontons claim that positive images usually have certain qualitative features, the cancer cells being depicted as weak and susceptible to breakdown, and the treatment as strong and powerful. They suggest that the body's immune system is depicted as aggressive, eager to 'do battle' with invading organisms and to destroy them, after which the person should see herself as healthy, free of disease, and able to reach her goals in life and fulfil her purpose. These features are clearly illustrated in young Joanne Gillespie's account of her fight against cancer:

> I visualise cancer cells as grey weak soldiers and my good cells as a strong white army of good fighters. I make the two armies fight and see all the grey soldiers smashed up and killed – no prisoners my mam and dad say – and I always make sure of that. Then a big waterfall runs right through my body washing away all the dead soldiers. I do this listening to music, sometimes soft music with no words. Then I visualise myself as I want to be – strong, healthy and dancing.

The Simontons suggest that those who succeed in overcoming cancer have or acquire imagery that matches these criteria. However, they also observe that imagery does not necessarily contain all these elements at the outset. People need to be helped to discover strong enough images to capture a new, positive expectation.

They indicate that it is especially important in overcoming malignancy that the most powerful imagery relates to the person's own natural defence system, rather than the disease or treatment. They propose that the individual should be encouraged to imagine the white blood cells of the body as at least as numerous and powerful as those of the malignancy, and they must also achieve powerful images of the latter being removed from the body. In addition, treatment must be visualised as a friend or ally, and patients encouraged to personalise it in any way that seems appropriate. It is suggested that this helps to reduce the side-effects of treatment, and there is some research evidence to support this claim. Given the need for vivid imagery, they recommend that the white cells are visualised as dogs voraciously eating minced meat (the cancer), and licking the area clean. However, it would seem that the Simontons fall into the very trap they advise others against inasmuch as they are not only imposing *their* imagery rather than encouraging people to generate their own, but also suggesting imagery of a curiously ambiguous nature. While to some people dogs may be 'man's best friend' people who are not 'dog lovers' or those who have experienced a dog bite may fear that such 'voracious' animals might not be satisfied with the meat and 'turn on' them.

Indeed, a good deal of the imagery recommended by the Simontons may provoke ambivalent responses. Current thinking is that the early work on the use of the imagination in the treatment of cancer placed too much emphasis on anger, killing and hating, and that as a result some people were repelled by it. It seems that because the Simontons' initial patient-group were in the armed forces and were not squeamish about 'attacking' and 'killing' cancer they assumed that everyone would be equally comfortable with these notions. In fact many people are profoundly disturbed by the idea of attacking and killing anything, even an invading disease organism. Words such as 'assault', 'kill', 'insult', 'blast', 'poison' and 'destroy' might therefore be rejected, either consciously or unconsciously, by some people. Left to summon their own imagery these people may very well devise equally effective but more gentle means of dealing with and disposing of their disease, which in the case of cancer is more appropriate because it is the body's own cells gone awry, and therefore a direct aggressive assault on them constitutes an attack on the person.

There are other reasons why gentler approaches are more appropriate. Although the immune system is commonly viewed as the body's defence system, designed to seek out and destroy harmful and alien substances such as bacteria and viruses, it is now recognised as functioning with more subtlety than this warlike metaphor suggests. Indeed, what has been described as the 'battlefield' terminology of immunology has to be reappraised in the light of evidence which suggests that, rather than being in any sense combative, the immune system operates co-operatively and collaboratively to support the integrity of the body and its optimal relationship to its environment.

From this perspective, disease can more appropriately be viewed as disharmony or lack of coherence rather than an unnatural disease-entity or state that needs to be fought.

Nevertheless, the healer Matthew Manning advocates 'fighting' imagery. He claims that many people who resist aggressive imagery often confuse anger with assertiveness, and that if there is any anger within a person and their imagery is passive then the anger has no release, whereas imagery that is initially aggressive becomes progressively less so as the anger is released. He also observes that the angry person is more powerful than the passive and that this strength may be used for healing.

8

ACKNOWLEDGING PAINFUL MESSAGES

Nothing in the world is meaningless; suffering least of all.

Oscar Wilde

It is one of the ironies of contemporary Western medicine that, despite the fact that pain is one of the most common symptoms doctors are required to deal with, they have very little understanding of it. A study reported in 1989 revealed that there is teaching on the subject of pain and its relief in only four out of twenty-one medical schools in Britain, and that even where taught, it is given only an average of 3.5 hours over a five-year medical course. Doctors receive little information on chronic pain syndromes, with the result that many patients, especially children and those suffering from cancer, often suffer unnecessarily because of outmoded medical training. Similarly, dentists receive little training in this area.

Orthodox medicine typically deals with pain by trying to suppress it with drugs or, in the case of persistent pain, to remove it through surgery. Neuro-surgeons have tended to view pain transmission as rather like a telephone system, the wires of which must be cut if incoming messages are to be prevented. Accordingly they often treat chronic pain by severing nerves, nerve roots, the spinal cord, and, when all else fails, by amputating limbs.

However, this approach has been overturned by the psychologist Ronald Melzack, who perceived that the 'telephone' model is totally inadequate. In his early research he

141

noted that dogs could be injured yet appear not to feel pain, and this led him to recognise that pain is not purely sensory or physical but a multi-dimensional experience, involving psychological and emotional factors such as attention, memory, expectation and training. The experience of pain thus depends on a number of variables other than the stimulus, some of which, like stress, anxiety or depression, can make the pain response more perceptible, while others, like relaxation and distraction, make it less so. He and his co-researcher, the physiologist Patrick Wall, therefore proposed that a nerve pathway exists which activates memories of past experiences and interacts with other pathways, effectively informing them which incoming signals are important and should be attended to in a given situation, and which are not. Depending on these criteria, signals from the body can be blocked or shut out at various points, preventing them reaching the major transmission centres of the brain and spinal cord and subsequently being felt. This mechanism, they suggest, explains why sports persons can often continue to perform despite severe injury. It also accounts for paradoxes such as the fact that many people severely wounded in battle feel no pain whatever, yet may find a routine injection very painful; while those unknowingly stabbed invariably feel little or no pain at the time of their injury. Ironically, therefore, a 'shot' may hurt a good deal more than actually being shot and a 'stabbing pain' produce greater anguish than being knifed.

These phenomena highlight the role of imagination and belief in the experience of pain. All the indications from both everyday experience and research are that opportunities to attend to and imagine the effects of a 'painful' stimulus generally guarantee a 'painful' response which might not otherwise be experienced, or at least not to the same degree. This is, of course, the basic principle of torture. Ironically it is also an intrinsic feature of many medical practices which encourage the individual to focus on pain, rather than distract attention away from it. Physicians routinely advise patients that 'this might hurt' when administering injections or taking blood, thereby sensitising them to pain; and, as has already been noted, they also 'programme' cancer patients to expect pain, discomfort, nausea and hair loss as 'normal' features of their treatment. However, perhaps the most obvious and common abuse of the 'torture principle' comes in childbirth, where women are explicitly encouraged to focus on 'the pains' rather than the pleasure and on the negative aspects of their experience rather than the positive.

Melzack and Wall's theory of pain control, which is now widely supported by research, essentially employs these psychological principles in reverse, that is, in the control rather than the enhancement of pain. Understanding of psychological factors in the experience of pain has led indirectly to the discovery of endorphin, the natural opiate-like pain-killing substance produced by the body, and to the development of psychological methods of pain control. Nevertheless, much of what is now known about pain does not reach the health-care practitioners who routinely deal with it. Within orthodox medicine pain is still objectified, and stripped of all subjective or psychological dimensions. Such a view is also widely held by the ordinary person in the street, as was highlighted for me recently when I overheard an exchange between two passing shoppers, one of whom replied to an enquiry made by the other with the remark: 'He's all right in himself, but he's in dreadful pain.'

Pain is generally conceived as something extrinsic to the person, to be controlled by physicians rather than dealt with in a way that would enable a person to take responsibility for it or to recognise its significance. Indeed, modern medicine tends to ignore the inherent meaning of pain. By comparison, traditional systems of healing recognise that pain is a non-verbal messenger *par excellence* – an alarm system to be acted on rather than against. These systems work with pain and attempt to learn from it rather than avoid it. In so doing they typically utilise a combination of relaxation and imagery.

Relaxation and imagery in the control of pain

The role of relaxation in pain control is increasingly being recognised. On the purely physical level, relaxation may alleviate the pain associated with involuntary muscle tension, which may be localised, more general or referred. Hence clenching the jaw may give rise to abdominal pain as well as headache and rigor of the jaw and neck; and low back pain may also implicate the buttock and leg muscles as a result of increased tension in these areas. While the primitive function of increased muscle tone might be to protect the pain site and prevent damaging movement, it is often unhelpful in pain not associated with injury or acute inflammation. Indeed, in non-acute pain the increased muscle tension often causes secondary pain which may exacerbate the original problem. Moreover, increased pain often interferes with relaxation and sleep, leading to an escalating spiral of tension and pain. Severe pain is also accompanied by subjective feelings of distress and physiological arousal which may be brought under control by successful relaxation training, and emphasis on breathing can also inhibit anxiety attacks and distress.

Relaxation can also have long-term physical effects. To the extent that relaxation constitutes greater muscle awareness or body sense, it can be viewed as a form of basic physical education which promotes a greater understanding of the relationships between muscle groups and of the effects of certain behaviours. Thus, a person may come to recognise that clenching and grinding the teeth, or lateral shifts of the jaw, creates tensions in the muscles of the temples, head and back which may be a significant factor in tension headache and migraine; and that tension in the diaphragm has implications for the abdomen and pelvis, causing pain in the hips and legs; while clenching the fists can effect the jaw, neck, head, chest and shoulders.

Clearly the reduction of physical tension can modify pain but the more subtle effects of relaxation may be equally or even more important. Relaxation of mental states and attitudes, everyday preoccupations and concerns – those mental tensions which ordinarily generate physical tensions – can be instrumental in reducing the experience of pain. As we have seen, this can be achieved through absorption either in bodily awareness or in imagery. There is now abundant evidence that certain activities and concomitant mental states can evoke changes in brain physiology, stimulating the pain-killing substance endorphin, the effects of which are similar to the drug morphine. It remains unclear whether this occurs as a direct result of relaxation or whether relaxation procedures help a person to ignore or dissociate from pain.

Absorption in relaxation procedures – whether those that focus solely on the body or those that employ imagery – modifies the sense of time, and this has implications for the experience of pain. Research suggests that any aversive or unpleasant experience shrinks the time sense. Pain, which clearly is both aversive *and* unpleasant, can therefore be relieved by expanding or relaxing the time sense. In effect this is what pain-killing drugs do; they kill pain by killing time, in much the way relaxation does. Thus, without being aware of it, most doctors who prescribe pain-killers are modifying the time sense. However, any activity that kills time can have pain-killing effects. Many athletes have described 'crossing the pain barrier' into pain-free, tranquil states. Hobbies and pastimes are often therapeutic for this reason as, of course, is imagery. There is empirical evidence for the role of the imagination in pain control (Achterberg and Lawlis, 1978). The combination of imagery and relaxation have been found to be more effective than other methods in reducing muscle tension and the need for pain-killing medications and sedatives in a number of conditions, including major burn injury. It has also been demonstrated to consistently lower pain levels during childbirth by about 30 per cent, which is as good as, or better than, conventional medications (Moon and Moon, 1984).

Hypnosis and pain control

Hypnosis, which combines relaxation and imagery, has long been recognised as a potent analgesic or pain-killer, and employed in numerous applications including childbirth and terminal illness (see also chapter 3). Hypnosis has been found to be better than acupuncture, Valium, aspirin or placebos in the relief of experimentally induced pain, and its effects more or less equivalent with morphine. As a result it is being used with increasing frequency to control the pain associated with cancer, and to reduce pain following major surgery. Its pain-reducing effects are often augmented by suggestions of warmth and comfort, which may also be important in providing relief.

Autogenic Training and pain modification

Another approach that employs a combination of relaxation and imagery in the control of pain is Autogenic Training, which was developed during the 1930s by the German neurologist and psychiatrist Johannes Schulz. This is a form of self-help therapy based on research into hypnosis that involves the induction of a highly relaxed state through focused attention on parts of the body specified in a number of physiologically adapted suggestions. Amongst its numerous applications Autogenic Training has been used to modify the pain threshold in different parts of the body and to block the pain of dental drilling. It has been widely researched and applied within Europe, and more recently in the USA and Japan, and although introduced only relatively recently into Britain it is becoming more widely practised within orthodox medicine.

Meditation and pain control

Meditation is also being more widely applied within orthodox medicine then formerly, largely as a result of research that has demonstrated its uses in controlling pain and other adverse features of cancer. Nevertheless, Western medicine has been slow to acknowledge the therapeutic applications of meditation in the control of pain, despite these effects having been demonstrated through intensive research since the 1930s. Studies of highly practised meditators have shown that they do not respond to extremes of heat or cold or being burned with hot glass tubing, and can raise their pain threshold quite considerably at will. Feats such as lying on beds of nails, walking on hot coals and sticking swords through various parts of the body are also demonstrable using similar methods, and it is now clear that these effects are achieved through control of the autonomic system, which is normally considered to be beyond voluntary control, by using relaxation and imagery.

Imagery not only has important implications for the control of pain through its effects on the autonomic nervous system, but also has an important function in facilitating the translation of the pain messages the latter generates. In so doing it may reveal that much pain is in fact psychological rather than physical in origin.

Pain as punishment

The term pain derives from the Latin *poena* meaning punishment, and while historically and socially it has often been inflicted upon others for precisely this purpose it is commonly not recognised that a good deal of pain is self-inflicted, albeit unconsciously. Dr Brian Roet, formerly a psychotherapist in the Pain Clinic of St Thomas's Hospital, London, and now in private practice, observes that this is frequently the case in those who suffer chronic pain or intermittent pain of great severity that defies medical explanation. He identifies a common pattern in business executives and other professionals of severe migraine or other pain that tends to recur at weekends, holidays and leisure events in the absence of any pathological or organic cause, antecedent factors, or conscious problem. However, further examination by way of hypnosis or other imaginative methods often reveals a profound guilt about taking time off from work, and that the pain is a form of unconscious punishment for so doing, or for other misdemeanours. So, just as illness may be an unconscious way of meeting needs, pain may be an indication of an unconscious need to punish oneself. Through imagery, therefore, it is often possible to identify psychological causes obscure to the conscious mind, and ways of treating them. Roet reports a case that clearly illustrates such an approach.

An attractive young woman of twenty was referred to him after having seen numerous medical consultants, none of whom could find any reason or means of relief for the severe recurrent migraine attacks which she had experienced from the age of ten. A review of her circumstances revealed a happy family background, good career prospects and social life and a loving fiancé to whom she was shortly to be married. The only problem appeared to be the debilitating headaches, which upon further examination seemed to occur prior to pleasurably anticipated events and occasions, leading Roet to conclude that they might be a self-inflicted punishment. At a conscous level this appeared not to be the case, with the client being unable to remember any incident or experience for which she might reasonably be punishing herself. However, under hypnosis she recalled just such an incident which had occurred when she was aged ten: the theft of some money from a member of her family, long forgotten at a conscious level, and long forgiven by everyone concerned – except herself, of course. The punishment she had inflicted on herself – quite unconsciously – was painfully to forego pleasure.

Through imagery this young woman was able to remember events and emotions that were inaccessible to her conscious mind and, similarly, she was able to use imagery to deal with the problem. Roet suggested that she 'try' her case in an imaginary court of law. Having done so she was able to accept that the punishment she had meted out to herself was disproportionate to the original 'crime' and had been served in full. She decided to pay the stolen sum of money to a charity – a small price to pay for what proved to be the complete remission of her headaches.

Methods which combine relaxation and imagery can therefore be seen to have several possible functions in alleviating and understanding pain:

- reducing pain by relieving tension;
- developing personal awareness of pain pathways and networks in the body;
- stimulating natural pain-killing substances in the body;
- helping to divert attention or dissociate from pain;
- modifying the time sense;
- influencing the autonomic and peripheral nervous systems;
- 'translating' pain messages.

The Simontons (see the previous chapter), very much in the manner of traditional healers, recognised these functions and adapted the methods developed initially by shamans and subsequently by modern pain researchers for use by cancer patients. Essentially their approach involves facilitating the patients' confrontation and communication with their pain directly through visualisation, so as to understand and control it. They claim that this enhances relaxation, helping to break the cycle of fear and tension that often builds up and overwhelms those suffering serious illness, and that with their fear reduced it is easier for them to develop a more positive expectation, which in turn serves further to reduce their fear. Thus the patients' visualisation of their pain augments and reinforces other psychological methods of self-healing. Moreover, as they relax and become more calm, pain takes a more background role and, with less of their energy taken up in fighting pain and fears, individuals become stronger and are able to invest more energy in their everyday life and its enjoyment. Thus, even for those with terminal cancer the quality of life may be greatly improved.

Exercise 8
Confronting and communicating with pain through imagery

Relax as fully as possible using whichever means you find most congenial. Having done so, identify areas of residual pain or those in which pain tends to recur. Imagine a tiny version of yourself shrinking down in size until able to enter that area through the pores of the skin and explore it thoroughly. As you focus your attention on the pain there, allow it to assume a shape. As it does, pay close attention to every aspect of its appearance, noting what you can learn from it. You may find that you can converse with it. If so, ask it what it is doing there and why, what it is doing for you or can do for you, and whether there is anything you can do for it. Pay close attention to any responses, remembering that they may be non-verbal or symbolic rather than verbal.

When you have learned as much from it as you can, imagine the pain shrinking in size, then experiment with modifying it in various ways, for example changing its shape, colour or texture, and noting any sensations in your body, or any thoughts, memories, or impressions that come to mind. Having effected as many changes as you can, then project the pain as far from your body as you can and observe it, noting as you do so any physical, emotional or mental reactions. When you have done this, allow the pain to return to its former position in your body, noting any changes in sensation, and return to ordinary awareness. Take some time to record your experience.

Commentary

Many people who attend courses or workshops on self-healing do so in the hope that they may be able to alleviate or control chronic pain, and in any group there are inevitably a number of people who suffer persistent and often intense pain. Nevertheless, a number will be sceptical about the effectiveness of imagery in the control of pain, even though they need no persuasion as to the value of imagery in other areas. For some, fear of failure or of having their hopes dashed may lead to a certain reluctance to attempt these exercises, or to do so wholeheartedly, but in other cases it is difficult to avoid the conclusion that they are 'at pains' to retain their pain. This raises the question of the usefulness their pain has for them in avoiding everyday responsibilities and opportunities, or simply as a conversation piece. It is difficult to conceive what some people would or could talk about if they had no aches and pains to complain about. Most of us take these 'painful' conversations for granted. They are an everyday fact of life, and we are often more acquainted with the vagaries of Mary's 'knee' or Arthur's 'back' than with any other feature of their lives. Indeed, we may know them rather better than we know their owners. So used are Mary or Arthur to the notion that they 'have' a pain, that they fail to recognise that they 'are' a pain, that is, not only a source of irritation to others, but also that their pain is a feature of their entire being, not an isolated condition.

A fascinating example of the functional aspect of pain was provided at a recent healing seminar I attended. Matthew Manning successfully and impressively demonstrated healing on a woman who had suffered severe restriction of movement and peristent pain in her arm for a number of years following surgery for cancer. On returning to her seat in the auditorium with the pain removed and her mobility restored, she turned to the person sitting next to her and said with a sigh, 'Well,

I suppose I will have to start doing the housework and shopping again.' A little later she assured a number of people, and no doubt herself, that while she could presently feel no pain, she expected it to return before long.

Relaxation may be sufficient to reduce or remove pains created through tension. However, it may also be sufficient to alert a person to pains of which they were formerly unaware or only vaguely conscious. Relaxation may thus create a space in which a person 'hears' what they have previously ignored or dismissed. It is not unusual, therefore, for people to discover just how painful their habitual tension is. Against this background of sub-acute pain other pains or warning signs can all too easily remain undetected. In some cases people discover that a pain about which they have been concerned for some time is the result of muscle tension. Typically this has resulted in a classic spiral whereby the initial pain gave rise to anxiety, which increased the tension that caused the pain in the first place, generating further fears about the pain getting worse, and so on. The disappearance of pain through relaxation is therefore usually greatly reassuring, and often permanent.

Awareness of the effects of tension in the various muscle groups in the body can have a similar effect. Although people are usually familiar with the idea that 'the knee-bone's connected to the thigh-bone' (if only because of the song), they generally are not aware that the connective tissue comprises muscles and tendons. Recognition of the interconnectedness of apparently remote 'bits and pieces' of themselves often comes as a surprise, and provides insight into the body parts implicated in various aches and pains.

The imagery generated by focusing on a pain can yield immediate benefits. People picture their pains in ways that often lend themselves to mental manipulation or modification. Thus a person may perceive his neck as a series of cogs that are jammed, and by mentally 'oiling' them can obtain relief. Similarly vices can be released, knots untied, muscles ironed, and so on. Mental absorption in the imaging process is in itself often sufficient to relax the tense areas and produce immediate relief, and it is also possible that the imagery influences physiology directly through right-brain processes.

151

The various modifications of the imagery such as shrinking it and projecting it from the body may also be very effective. In so doing, many people discover that they have some degree of control over their perception of pain, and therefore their experience of it. Others discover that they can dissociate from it. One woman reported that, having projected her long-standing pain so far away from her body that she could no longer 'see' it, she realised she could no longer feel it either, and therefore refused to replace it within her body. Some might argue that relief from pain achieved in this way is only short term and that the pain will return. Certainly if one expects the pain to recur it very probably will, as this is tantamount to inviting it to do so. However, if people can achieve even fleeting relief from pain, this may be sufficient to convince them that they have the power to control it and through practice can extend the pain-free periods. One of the most dramatic examples of the effectiveness of this method of pain control came from an elderly woman who had received every conceivable treatment for pain relief that was available, including a twelve-month intensive programme at a pain clinic, without success. She was understandably overjoyed when during and after this exercise she was relieved of her pain for the first time in many years. She described being able to 'see' her pain floating 'disembodied' outside her, but being unable to feel it. She felt confident that having discovered how to achieve this she could train herself to dissociate from the pain completely.

It may seem that such a method of dealing with pain runs counter to the idea that pain is a warning message which should be listened to and acted upon. However, Melzack and Wall have indicated that as a result of psychological factors pain can not only be more easily perceptible, but can become entirely disproportionate to the degree of actual tissue damage and persist long after injured tissues have healed. So, they observe, 'rather like a broken car horn' pain may not be blaring any useful warning. In such cases an alternative to 'turning off' the horn is to distract attention away from it. The problem for most people is that rather than distracting themselves from pain they become obsessed by it, often to the extent that it distracts them from everything else. This frequently occurs with tinnitus, a condition where a person suffers persistent ringing, hissing or booming sensations in one or both ears. Although not usually physically painful as such, it creates tremendous psychological distress, often described by sufferers as 'agony' or 'torture'. Many of those so afflicted are unable to sleep or relax because of the incessant noise, with the result that their tension and distress escalates and their attention becomes increasingly focused on the problem that threatens to overwhelm them.

However, tinnitus sufferers can derive considerable relief through psychological methods which help them to relax and dissociate from the ever-present noise. Effectively they learn to turn down the 'radio' blaring in their head and to get on with other things. The condition is in no sense 'cured' but it does become more manageable. A man who described himself as on the verge of a nervous breakdown following the onset of tinnitus, which had resulted in the loss of a prestigious job and many ordinary pleasures, reported that after only six attempts at the combined relaxation/imagery exercise he was able to read for sustained periods – something which he had previously found impossible – and was able to resume a more normal life. He became so enthusiastic about psychological methods that he subsequently established a tinnitus self-help and support group to introduce other sufferers to them.

While dissociating from pain may have its undoubted uses in severe or chronic pain, in the majority of cases confronting the issue is considerably more beneficial than avoiding it. A particularly effective way of doing so is not simply to view it or gain a different perspective on it through imagery but to communicate with it directly. Some people are reluctant to speak to their knee or back, perhaps because from childhood they have been told that talking to oneself is the first sign of madness, and they consequently consider such an activity crazy. What is perhaps more crazy is that most people seem not to regard their bodies as part of themselves in the same way that their minds are. Consequently they see intelligence as confined to the brain rather than pervading the body as a whole, and don't avail themself of its wisdom. Hence they don't listen to the body. However, when they do, they are often astonished by the outcome. Having complained for some time of a painful right shoulder, I was advised to take a dose of my own medicine and listen to it, which I promptly did by asking my shoulder what was wrong with it. Immediately I had a strong memory-image of myself as a schoolgirl walking home with a heavy satchel on my shoulder, and I received a 'reply' to the effect that the right side of my body always 'shoulders' burdens, notably those of an academic kind, and is often weighed down with work. I then realised that in the previous three months I had completed several draft chapters of a textbook – by hand – but I had not made any connection between it, the writing and my shoulder. I therefore decided to use a typewriter for the remaining chapters and my shoulder pain disappeared. Now, whenever I experience a pain in my shoulder, I ask myself whether I am working too hard, or going about it in the wrong way.

Some people find that when their pains take shape it is that of a person known to them, often a relative or spouse. One woman identified her 'pain in the neck' as her dependent mother, and another described the pain in her chest as her mother lying across the length of her collar bone. Indeed mothers and mothers-in-law frequently manifest as pains in the neck, chest and back, usually of those women who are charged with the task of looking after them. It is perhaps not surprising that people who are perceived as burdens produce pains in those who do so.

Daughters compete with mothers as 'pains'. Several women who have described their daughters in these terms have located their effects in the chest. One woman found herself stifled by her daughter, quite literally, and experienced not only chest pains but breathing difficulties and bronchitis in her presence. Another mother associated her angina with visits from her married daughter. Frequently these physical pains are the only expression these women have for their ambivalent or downright hostile attitudes to their offspring. It is not the 'done thing' for mothers to express dislike of their children, and so they often find it difficult to admit, even to themselves, the 'heartache' they experience in their relationships with them. This is true also of those who, because of religious beliefs or affiliation, are opposed to divorce and unable to admit to their profoundly unhappy relationships. Interestingly, when men experience similar difficulties they seem to manifest in their nether regions – lower back, buttocks and bowels – suggesting perhaps that they tend to suppress these feelings by 'sitting on them'.

The distinction between physical and emotional pain is often very subtle indeed, so much so that when doing this exercise many people find themselves confronting deep emotional hurt manifesting as physical pain. As one young woman said, 'Every time I focus on my physical pains I find that it is actually my feelings that are hurt.' Typically loss of some kind is discovered: loss of a baby or child, a relationship or marriage, job, status or self-respect, or loss of a loved one through death. Almost invariably the initial hurt has been covered up, often very quickly, rather than being exposed and aired, and, as in the case of a hastily applied sticking-plaster, contaminating factors may have been sealed in and buried. Thus although on the surface the issue appears to have been dealt with, real healing has not necessarily taken place. In many cases the wound has continued to fester beneath the plaster, sometimes producing problems out of all proportion to the original hurt. These may erupt much later and not be recognised as having any connection with the original trauma, or they may simply poison the whole system.

Grieving may have taken place, albeit cursorily, so that the loss appears to have been dealt with, but anger relating to it has not been discharged. This unexpressed anger then festers as resentment, and while anger is neutral, and only positive or negative depending on *how* it is expressed, resentment is always negative and unhealthy. Indeed, as has been noted previously, resentment often proves deadly, being associated with various serious diseases, including cancer. The tendency to effect hasty cover-ups of normal, healthy emotions therefore often leads to malignancy, and the process is all too frequency assisted by the medical practice of prescribing tranquillisers and anti-depressants to those experiencing loss or bereavement.

For many people, resentment develops because they have

never aired their feelings and have therefore not identified them appropriately. They therefore assume they are sad when in fact they are intensely angry. One woman, speaking of her son who had died tragically in an accident, startled herself by saying, 'And if he were alive now I'd kill him' – not only because he had died pursuing a dangerous hobby she disapproved of, but also because his death had prevented her from realising personal ambitions. Another mother who had lost a teenage son in a motoring accident admitted to being 'consumed' by resentment towards the car driver, who had survived.

Whether the initial trauma relates to death, sexual or physical abuse in childhood, or loss of face, there is invariably anger about what has been taken away. This anger, if not expressed or brought to the surface as resentment at being left alone, childless, jobless, penniless and much else, will continue to eat away at the person unless or until it can be excised. As has been noted previously, breast cancer sufferers are very commonly characterised by unexpressed anger and resentment. One woman, whose rapidly growing cancer of the breast followed a protracted work-related difficulty, provided a classic metaphor when she reported being so resentful on seeing former work colleagues that she 'bust'. Woody Allen (cited by Siegel, 1990) puts it another way: 'I can't express anger. I internalize it and grow a tumor instead.'

If healing is to be effected these hurt feelings must be dealt with, and treated with as much respect as tissue damage. Failure to do so may result ultimately in far greater pain. Imagery provides a most important means of dealing with these issues, which are often difficult to access by more conventional verbal means, not only because society does not encourage their expression, but because they are by their very nature non-verbal and emotional, and easily repressed. Imagery is thus a necessary tool for examining and excising the contents of the unconscious mind, as shamans since the earliest times have recognised. It is a highly potent therapy – and as Lawrence LeShan has observed, if a therapy is strong enough to help it is strong enough to hurt. This prospect may be alarming to some people, but it has to be remembered that it is a tool within the person's control, and as such essentially non-invasive and non-intrusive. Nevertheless, when used to probe deep emotions, pains and fears, it must be used sensitively. Rather like the removal of a splinter or thorn in the flesh, it is usually best done by the person himself. The individual is the best judge of the process.

9

TUNING IN TO INNER WISDOM AND GUIDANCE

This demon, that's the spirit that keeps thee, is noble, courageous, high, unmatchable.
William Shakespeare (Anthony and Cleopatra)

In many of the archaic traditions of the world one encounters the idea of some principle or force in the psyche which gives shape and structure to human life, influencing, directing and regulating it, while functioning below conscious awareness so that its processes are to a great extent unknown to the conscious mind. Nevertheless, it communicates with the conscious self by way of feelings, intuitions, dreams and imagery. Throughout history this inner world has been commented upon by poets and philosophers, and investigation of it has long been the province of religion and of occultism, which is concerned with the development of techniques for accessing this hidden realm.

The traditional role of the shaman was to master and utilise these methods in order to divine the inner world, hence their claims to be able to enter into the 'underworld', there to commune with energies that they characterised in various ways as either human or animal spirits. Identified thus, these energies were then cultivated as 'inner guides' to help them explore the inner world of others. Numerous means were employed for so doing, including drugs, dancing and meditation, all of which essentially put the shamans beyond ordinary conscious processes – and thus out of their minds in the normal sense – and in contact with what might be thought of as living energies containing information and ideas. With the growth of rationalism in Western cultures such methods were quickly dismissed and this source of information or knowledge undervalued and ignored.

To a great extent, therefore, Western man became cut off from a source of knowledge which remains highly valued in the East and in other cultures where the rationalist philosophy and tradition are less well established. Nevertheless, many significant figures in the history of Western civilisation have acknowledged this inner wisdom or guidance and the means by which it is acquired or accessed. One of the most notable was Socrates, who described having since childhood a 'constant companion' or prophetic inner voice which communicated instructions on what or what not to do that were always reliable. This voice would interrupt his normal train of thought or conversation, or could be accessed intentionally through trance or contemplation. He assumed this 'daemon', as he termed it, to be a minor deity or divine messenger, and he was in no doubt that other people also had personal daemons.

This idea found its way into Christianity in the third century via St Gregory, who also described his divine companion. However, as *daemon* was essentially pagan, the term angel (from the Greek *angelus*, meaning messenger) came into usage, and the notion of a guardian angel or guide persists within Christianity and is still widely subscribed to.

An immanent spiritual self or Higher Self which can be realised through inner knowing was also emphasised in the Neoplatonic tradition, and the notion of spirit guides is discernible in the Mystery traditions and throughout the Renaissance. Dante described his inner journey and his guides Virgil and Beatrice in *The Divine Comedy*, and a similar process is represented symbolically by the Sephiroth in the Jewish mystical tradition of the Kabbalah. However, during the Middle Ages the term daemon took on the connotation of the devil's agent, and, through association as it were, angels became increasingly suspect.

Angels were acceptable as long as the guidance they imparted was consistent with that of the Church and authorities acting in its name, but where it was in conflict they were seen as sources of heresy. The fate of Joan of Arc, who claimed that God's instructions were transmitted to her by three guardian angels, Saints Catherine, Margaret and Michael, and the widespread purge on witches, discouraged others from admitting to inner voices or 'familiars'. Indeed to do so, given the consequences, could justifiably be regarded as a sign of insanity, and so by the nineteenth century those who claimed to hear voices or receive inner guidance were committed to asylums. Ironically therefore one encounters the paradox whereby a person who claims to talk to God was, and still is, described as praying and considered righteous, whereas a person who claims that God talks to him is regarded as mad and possibly evil.

Even so, the idea of a guiding or protective force did not disappear. Brian Inglis, in his historical account of this phenomenon, *The Unknown Guest*, suggests that belief in this principle was retained because most people at some time in their lives experience what seems like a personal intervention, protecting or prompting them. He classifies these experiences into three categories, namely: *the daemon*, the feeling of a prompter as a lifelong companion, which might not necessarily be recognised as such until a succession of meaningful coincidences, premonitions, intuitions and inspirations (and, sometimes, setbacks) leads to the feeling that there is some form of guidance at work; *the muse*, traditionally regarded as a source of inspiration for artists and writers (so much so that it used to be fashionable to begin a poem with an invocation to the muse); and *the Eureka effect*, which performs a similar service for mathematicians and scientists.

Inglis claims that for most people intimations of daemonic influence occur only occasionally and erratically, via hallucinations of the senses, visions and premonitions, while for others the influence is more sustained. This claim is supported by the findings of the Koestler Foundation, which has collected and analysed evidence for the activities of this 'unknown guest' (a term first coined for these experiences by the Nobel laureate Maurice Maeterlink). Among those who have acknowledged some guiding force at work in their lives are many distinguished people, such as Churchill who, as Inglis indicates, attributed to it his escape from captivity

160

during the Boer War and from a bomb incident during World War II. Many writers, artists and musicians throughout history have attributed their inspiration to a muse, and most leading scientists, including Newton, Swedenborg, Poincaré, Einstein, Planck, Pauli, Schrödinger and Heisenberg, have acknowledged their debt to a similar principle (Inglis, 1987). Indeed, rather than disappearing, the daemon simply became couched in terms more acceptable to a culture in which science progressively overtook the divine as the source of all wisdom.

The concept of the unconscious

The concept of unconscious mental processes was conceived in about 1700, became very popular by 1800, and was commonplace by 1870. Over a century ago the psychologist and philosopher Frederick Myers drew particular attention to what he termed the subliminal mind – that part lying below the threshold of consciousness – claiming that it is capable of performing in many of the ways of the conscious mind or ego, to such an extent that it is possible to conceive of it as the subliminal *self*, which, albeit part of a larger self, is capable of acting independently. He believed the subliminal self to be superconscious in that it is capable of gathering information through extra-sensory means, including telepathy. He suggested that if it breaks into consciousness uncontrolled it can produce the signs of genius. He accepted, however, that it often has to struggle to break through to consciousness and so resorts to what is thought of as intuition, and it is this which leaves the impression of a prompter at work.

Sigmund Freud

Freud, who is often, quite wrongly, credited with having discovered the unconscious, conceived of mind as comprising energy in two forms, mobile and bound, both originating in bodily processes which he equated with sexuality. He regarded the former as characteristic of unconscious mental processes and as chaotic and unstructured, but the latter, characteristic of conscious mental processes, as structured and organised. He believed that unconscious impulses, ideas and emotions strive energetically to become conscious but are prevented from doing so by the action of various mechanisms which defend the conscious mind, or ego, from them. Accordingly personality is a defence against these unconscious strivings. Freud therefore advocated conscious control of them by putting people in touch with the landscapes of their mind, which was achieved through introversion, or looking inward.

Freud himself admitted (at his seventieth birthday celebrations) to not having discovered or even rediscovered the unconscious, but he claimed to have discovered and developed a method by which it could be studied. However, even this claim is controvertible because in its early stages his approach was similar to meditation and contemplation, and the role of the therapist he advocated very similar to that of the shaman. His methods were also similar, involving evocations and interpretation of imagery through hypnosis, fantasy and dreams, the latter being regarded by Freud as of particular importance and described by him as 'the royal road to the unconscious'.

However, far from welcoming any comparison between his practices and those of shamans, Freud would have been outraged because he had a horror of the occult, and for this reason went to considerable lengths to describe his theory and methods in terms consistent with the science of his time. It was Freud's refusal to acknowledge that science had anything to gain from ancient occult sources which led to the breach of his friendship and collaboraton with the psychiatrist Carl Jung.

Carl Jung

Independently of Freud, Jung had conceived of a personal subconscious or unconscious comprising emotions, ideas and memories that are pushed below the threshold of the conscious mind because of the individual's reluctance to acknowledge them – complexes that tend to break away from the general unity of the psyche and become dissociated. He also conceived of a deeper level of the unconscious where reside primordial or archaic images, emotions and thoughts that he termed archetypes, which are shared by all humanity. Accordingly the individual conscious mind is merely the tip of a vast iceberg, an apparently independent feature of a submerged realm – the collective unconscious.

Like Freud, Jung conceived of mind in terms of energy, and mental health as a point of equilibrium on a continuum between opposite poles. He held that unless this is achieved and maintained, energy lost by consciousness passes into the unconscious, effectively tilting the balance in that direction. This energy gradient activates the contents of the unconscious, transforming the material from the collective unconscious into intuitions which intrude upon consciousness in dreams, fantasy and visions, and may, if sufficiently energised, erupt into consciousness, provoking neurosis and psychosis. However, normal consciousness can be turned inward and work on the contents of the unconscious, enabling them to develop and become understood. For Jung this was important because he believed that, as long as unconscious content is not understood, it keeps intruding into consciousness, and is more likely to overwhelm consciousness if repressed.

Jung therefore advocated introversion of the conscious mind for the purpose of rendering the unconscious comprehensible. He saw this process, which he termed active imagination, as a training in switching off conscious thought and allowing unconscious content to develop. In Jung's approach, therefore, the aim of psychological development is the integration of both the conscious and unconscious aspects of the self, which must be worked on simultaneously so that rejected or dissociated features can be rediscovered and reintegrated into the whole. He termed this process of reintegration 'individuation', and he regarded it as synonymous with wholeness or health. He recognised that man, as a symbolic animal, can resolve even the most deep divisions within himself on the symbolic plane, and he developed a means of psychotherapy whereby this could be accomplished. Jungian therapy therefore comprises various techniques for deliberately mobilising active imagination or creativity.

These include painting, modelling, sculpture and dance. He emphasised the importance of both therapist and client working collaboratively on the interpretation of these products, rather than the latter remaining the passive recipient of the therapist's interpretation. Like Freud, Jung regarded dreams as very important, but he also regarded fantasy highly. His therapeutic approach therefore has many parallels with that of shamans. Indeed Jung has been described as the greatest magician of the modern age. His therapy operates in much the same way as magic on the non-verbal level of pictures and images, accessing the unconscious mind through archaic symbolism and ritual, and thereby producing changes in consciousness.

The Jungian approach is, however, different from shamanism, primarily because, unlike the shaman, the Jungian therapist does not take on the role of guide, but merely initiates the process of introversion, after which the individual undertakes inner work alone, becoming independent of the therapist and autonomous.

Roberto Assagioli

The Italian psychiatrist Roberto Assagioli also viewed the unconscious as a source of potential and wisdom, and believed that people should be sufficiently in communication with the deep forces within their psyche to be able to use them, rather than be used by them. Like Jung, he felt that Freudian interpretation of unconscious imagery introduced an undesirable passive element into the therapeutic relationship, so he used guided imagery, day-dreams or symbols, which allowed his patients themselves to mediate between conscious and unconscious material. He conceived of symbols as 'containers' of meaning, as transformers and conductors, or channels, of psychic energies. For Assagioli as for Jung, wholeness or health requires the integration or synthesis of imagination, intuition and inspiration with rational, conscious processes. However, despite their profound importance to human experience and scientific endeavour, modern psychology has deemed these three 'Is' to be 'unscientific' areas of study because they are not susceptible to laboratory investigation or quantitative analysis, and has dismissed them almost totally in favour of the study of overt behaviour.

Ironically, most of the leading scientists of the century have little doubt as to the importance of the unconscious mind. The Nobel-prize-winning physicist Wolfgang Pauli insisted that the laws of nature cannot be discovered empirically from the given data, but require intuition, which must be fed from the store of primeval images whose resources cannot be accessed through logic. His fellow Nobel laureate Roger Sperry also argues that neurological research on the relationship of mind and brain compels a direct break with the long-established materialistic and behaviourist doctrine of the West, and necessitates an acceptance of intuition as the key reality. It is only recently and only in some quarters, however, that psychology has turned its attention to this area and acknowledged that, just as understanding the whole truth of the universe requires the use of intuition, so also does personal wholeness or health. Given that this insight is essentially that of ancient man, it is not surprising that many of the techniques that have been developed for so doing bear many resemblances to the archaic methods of the shamans.

It is now increasingly acknowledged that it is the severance from the inner resources of the unconscious and its processes that leads or contributes to illness. Widespread experience in the field of healing suggests that many recovered and recovering patients have come to see their illness as, in part, a message to value and pay more attention to their unconscious self and its needs. Many people have described specific insights or feelings derived from dreams or other imagery which have provided them with invaluable guidance in their attempts to regain or maintain health.

Tapping unconscious processes for healing

Carl Simonton and Stephanie Simonton-Atchley recognise that the unconscious mind contains resources that can be mobilised in support of personal growth and healing. They thus teach a process, the Inner Guide visualisation, which is a guided fantasy for tapping these rich resources of strength and healing, and they provide numerous anecdotal accounts of those who have overcome serious illness by following this inner guidance. The Simontons claim that visualising an inner guide provides access to the unconscious because it is a symbolic representation of aspects of the self not normally available during conscious awareness. Thus when contacting the inner guide through mental imagery a person is held to be connecting with important mental sources from which they are normally cut off.

For many, the inner guide takes the form of a respected authority figure or highly symbolic character with whom the person conducts an internal conversation, asking questions and receiving answers that seem wise beyond the individual's conscious capacities. Moreover, it is claimed, people are often more responsive to the insights derived from consultation with their inner guide than with their therapists or doctors, which is to be encouraged because, as the inner guide is an aspect of the patient's personality, reliance on it is seen as a healthy step towards taking responsibility for physical and psychological health.

The Simontons present the case of John, an 18-year-old with leukaemia, whom they describe as withdrawn, overtly intellectual, and believing that problems which cannot be solved rationally are insoluble. One night he had a dream in which an 'unorthodox doctor' appeared and indicated that he wanted to help him overcome his disease. Encouraged by the Simontons to view this internal healer as a representation of his own powers of recovery, he continued to consult it about his problems through mental imagery. As a result of the advice received, he requested, and was given, a high-protein food which enabled him to put on weight, and had an exercise programme devised for him which improved his overall condition, activity and morale. His experience, along with that of others with their inner guide, has led the Simontons to describe the process as 'uniformly valuable in aiding patients' recoveries'.

It is not merely patients suffering serious illness who can benefit from this process, as the surgeon Bernie Siegel relates in his best-selling book *Love, Medicine and Miracles*. He attributes the radical change in his practice of medicine to his initial experience of the Inner Guide exercise during a teaching seminar run by the Simontons. As he explains:

> I approached this exercise with all the scepticism one expects from a mechanistic doctor. Still I sat down, closed my eyes and followed directions. I didn't believe it would work, but if it did I expected to see Jesus or Moses. Who else would dare appear inside a surgeon's head?
>
> Instead I met George, a bearded, long-haired young man wearing an immaculate flowing white gown and skullcap. It was an incredible awakening for me, because I hadn't expected anything to happen. As the Simontons taught us to communicate with whomever we'd called up from our unconscious minds, I found that talking to George was like playing chess with myself, but without knowing what my alter ego's next move would be.
>
> George was spontaneous, aware of my feelings, and an excellent advisor. He gave me honest answers, some of which I didn't like at first.
>
> I was still toying with the idea of a career change. When I told him, he explained that I was too proud to give up the hard-won technical proficiency of surgery and start from scratch on another discipline. Instead, he told me, I could do more good by remaining a surgeon but changing my *self* to help my patients mobilize their mental powers against disease. I could combine the support and guidance of a minister or psychiatrist with the resources and expertise of a physician . . . I suppose you may call George a 'meditatively released insight from my unconscious', or some such, if you must have an intellectual label for him. All I know is that he has been my invaluable companion ever since his first appearance. My life is much easier now, because he does the hard work.

Siegel goes on to report how George not only helped him to see things about medicine that he'd missed before, and thus to discover his true career in healing, but also enabled him to speak spontaneously about his approach to healing rather than using prepared lectures when he addressed large audiences.

The actress Shirley MacLaine has also described using inner guides to help her as a public speaker and spokesperson for inner transformation and healing:

I felt naked and vulnerable before the crowd of people, except for the twenty-five page security blanket of a speech clutched in my hands. I looked out at them as they settled and hushed. Suddenly I knew I would lose this audience if I referred to that speech even once. So I made a decision. After acknowledging their applause, I put the speech down on the table behind me. I took another deep breath, and stood, waiting. The room became very still, currents of silent energy hovering, waiting. With my eyes open, I meditated asking for help. I knew I had guides and teachers. They might reside in an unseen dimension but they were nevertheless real to me. I allowed myself to believe that I was aligning with them and with a spiritual dimension that could see me through whatever was required to make pragmatic sense to everyone in the audience.

Many, many thoughts went through my mind in what was, in fact, a very brief time, but in that time, power seemed to flow into me and through me. I began to feel imbued with confidence. It was a glorious feeling. Not arrogant but richly confident . . .

That is exactly what happened at that first seminar, and, with variations, continued to happen through the years of seminars that followed.

The following exercise is a modification of the Inner Guide visualisation used by the Simontons.

Exercise 9
An Inner Guide visualisation

Sitting or lying comfortably with eyes closed take a few moments to draw your attention from your external surroundings to the inner realm of your thoughts, feelings and bodily sensations. Gradually allow these to drift away. Then, having done so, imagine that it is a bright, warm, spring day and that you are taking a walk in pleasant countryside. As you do so you are taking note of all the sights, sounds, smells and sensations of this season. You see the new growth of plants and trees, the fresh colours, hear the birds busy in the hedgerows and trees, and the lambs in the fields. You pause frequently to touch and smell flowers and grasses. As you walk along you feel a sense of renewal, promise, peace and well-being.

After some time you come to a path at the edge of a large meadow and you follow it, taking note of all you see, hear, smell and feel as you do so. Eventually the path leads into an area of broad-leaved woodland, where wide, closely-cropped green rides or pathways thread between the trees. Walking along one of these rides you find a large boulder and, feeling pleasantly warm and tired, you sit down upon it. For some time you enjoy the sights and sounds of nature, progressively experiencing yourself as at one with it.

As you do so you become aware of a radiant white light in the distance. It is gradually approaching you, but you are in no way threatened or alarmed by this. You simply observe it, and as it gets closer you see that it is taking shape, transforming into a person, creature or thing. You take careful note of all the details of its appearance, and how you react towards it. If you feel warm, safe, comfortable or other positive feelings, this is your Inner Guide. If, however, you feel negative feelings coming from it, dismiss it, and wait until a positive guide comes forward.

When it does ask its name. Take careful note of any response, remembering that it may be in the form of signs, symbols or images. If it seems reluctant to respond, assure it that you genuinely wish to know and learn from it.

Having established this initial contact ask if it has any advice or guidance for you, taking careful note of its response. Then ask if there is anything you can do for it.

If you are able to do so, establish a more lengthy dialogue, confiding your problems and asking its advice on them. Then thank your guide for being there and assisting you, and ask how and when you should make future contact with it. Once again take careful note of its responses.

Then allow the image to fade.

Imagine yourself sitting on the boulder and observe your feelings. Then retrace your steps through the wood and meadow, and gradually return to normal awareness. Take a few moments to record the details of your experience.

Commentary

The Simontons advise people not to be discouraged if they do not make contact with their guide or receive information from it on their first attempt. They observe that several attempts may be necessary for this to occur because this is an aspect of the self which may not have been attended to for years, and re-establishing communication may take time and patience.

I have found this to be true for only a small minority of workshop participants, and frequently it is those who are most eager to benefit from any advice or information they can glean from the exercise. Their desire or impatience may generate tension and anxiety which inhibits relaxation, re-engages their rational mind, or prevents them giving sufficient time for their imagery to develop.

When this occurs people frequently experience profound disappointment and despondency, which may in themselves be important indications of negativity – the belief that they have no such guide or inner resources ('poor me') – and expectation effects ('I might have known I wouldn't find a guide'). Some, on hearing the experiences of others, betray similar negativity ('It always happens to me', 'Why do I never get positive results?', 'Why can't I have a guide like theirs?') These reactions may have an important bearing on health and illness, because they suggest ways in which the individual typically responds to stressors.

The form the guide takes is as various as the individuals who carry out the exercise. A surprising number of people report being told that the light is a spirit. No doubt this reflects popular connotations about inner guides. Typically such people will say something along the lines of 'When you said this spirit was approaching . . .', or 'When you described the light forming into a spirit . . .'. They are usually convinced of this, and are only persuaded by other group members that these instructions have not been given. The 'spirit' may be a ghost-like figure, an angel, saint or prophet. Christ-like beings and madonnas are common. This tendency to perceive inner features of the self as spiritual may, however, be a prohibitive factor for some people. One man, a self-declared atheist, admitted being completely 'turned off' at the prospect of the white light, which he interpreted in religious terms, and disgusted by what he perceived as an attempt on my part to 'evangelise'. This spiritual paranoia often arises from a confusion between spirituality and religion, which is characteristic of Western culture, and is for many people a major barrier to their achieving contact with themselves. Religious or anti-religious attitudes and prejudices may therefore prevent the full and wholesome integration of an individual and their gaining insight into their problems. The man referred to above discontinued the exercise at the first suggestion (his) of the 'spirituo-religious', and emerged from it angry and hostile.

Awareness of the barriers which can be imposed by those for whom the inner guide implies mystical or religious beliefs has led some practitioners of imaginative medicine to encourage the development of creature-advisors – animals or fantasy figures – which might allow right-brain information to be accessed in problem solving, are also simple and demystify the process. Doctors at the UCLA Medical School Pain Clinic claim to have achieved much success using light-hearted fantasy figures as inner guides to be consulted as a source of information about pain. These are often humorous, cartoon-like animals, but despite their whimsical qualities they help individuals to identify factors in their life which may be contributing to pain. Although I have little doubt that these are effective (one of my clients having derived great benefit from a 'Roger Rabbit' character who gave her very sound advice on her condition), I prefer not to prescribe any images or image-categories in the belief that whatever the individual produces, or fails to produce, has personal significance. It may well be that the individual's difficulty with a certain image relates precisely to the feature which may be contributing to his or her pain or illness and needs to be addressed. As the Simontons observe, the figure that the individual is calling on is merely a symbol for the inner self: an intuitive, wise and responsive part of the self with which they are generally out of touch, and which, if accessed, may reveal how they are making themselves sick and how they can make themselves well.

Indeed, in the case of the man described above, subsequent group discussion led him to reappraise his definition of spirituality, and to consider the effect on his life of his denial of this aspect of himself. It transpired that, in denying the existence of an external God in the conventional Western sense, he had denied the possibility of any meaning in life, leaving himself with a classic existential anxiety and attendant feelings of despair, hopelessness, chronic depression and suicidal tendencies. His failure to acknowledge that he could

171

create his own meaning in life and take control of it by believing in himself (rather than God) is precisely the malaise which the Simontons are trying to overcome in cancer patients whose diagnosis has thrown them into a similar condition of hopelessness and despair. The discovery of an inner guide can in itself have profound effects on those who are depressed, helping them to overcome feelings of isolation and to draw upon reserves of hitherto unidentified resources.

Such was the case of a troubled young man with suicidal tendencies whose 'light', illuminating a golden pathway, led him forward through the trees and gave him hope and promise for the future. He subsequently admitted that this experience was a turning point for him in his return to health.

I have found that young people generally experience this exercise as revelatory. Typically their guide embraces them, giving them reassurance, feelings of love and acceptance, and an impression of great hope, promise and fruitfulness. In one case an inner guide in the form of a tree embraced the person, imbuing her with energy. In another the inner guide appeared as a light that created colourful flowers wherever it passed, suggesting perhaps similar advice to that given by Rabindranath Tagore: 'Do not linger to gather flowers to keep, but walk on, for flowers will keep themselves blooming all your way.'

A retired gentleman, however, reported what he described as one of the most remarkable emotional experiences of his life when his inner guide appeared as cherry blossom so deep that it threatened to overwhelm him, both in quantity and in the quality of its beauty, colour, scent and freshness.

Another man reported a rather less fragrant experience when his guide, in the shape of a drain pipe, hit him forcefully in the part of the abdomen where he typically experienced both recurrent tension and health problems. Although he was unable to understand its significance, various possibilities suggest themselves: that the tension there was a 'drain' on his energies, or that some 'drainage' of the area might be appropriate. (A subsequent medical examination indicated the latter, but clearly also had implications for the former.) One woman 'saw' nothing but 'felt' a presence and her long-standing pain being lifted from her body. Another woman saw a black thundercloud that enveloped her and gave her a feeling of a great strength – which, once again, illustrates the way in which the individual meaning of imagery needs to be sought, as for many people thunderous black clouds have negative or unpleasant associations.

For another woman the light transformed into a crystal ball which did nothing except 'play' warmly in her hands, indicating to her the importance of warmth and touch. In another instance, the light transformed into the same image encountered previously by the person in the Magic Shop – a jack-in-the-box – which she had been unable to understand but subsequently realised was a message to be more playful.

One man's light turned into a complete and unfamiliar scene: an arch, and beyond it a medieval village with a church to one side and houses on the other. Although he didn't understand it at the time, he felt absolutely compelled to investigate it further and to discover its meaning. Some people discern the inner guide's message very clearly but are not willing to act on it, perhaps because it compromises their view of how they should behave. Therefore admonitions to take it easy, look after oneself, slow down, lighten up, soften, enjoy life, be sexy, have fun, or retire, all tend to be dismissed as indulgent. By comparison, advice such as lose weight, take more exercise, relax, stop smoking or eating meat may be rejected for the opposite reason, as too stringent.

One young woman was very disturbed to be advised of the need to give more expression to her creative side. This she took as meaning that she should give up her non-creative job, which was unthinkable as she needed the financial support it provided and could not see any 'creative' alternative as in any way lucrative. Subsequent attempts at the exercise produced a similar response, with the message persisting until she acknowledged that the stress imposed by her present job was contributing in no small way to her ill health, and that she could achieve a compromise by continuing to work and engage in her creative pastimes for relaxation. Formerly she had experienced so much conflict when she attempted to do so that she had completely ceased all creative activities, denying a very important part of herself and also opportunities for relaxation. When she tried to effect the compromise as instructed she found that she gained a great sense of relief and release, and an improvement in her overall health and well-being. A year or so later she sent me a message, from which I learned that she had fulfilled her creativity by giving birth to a son a few days previously.

This all-or-nothing, black-or-white approach to life is very common and may contribute to ill health in various ways. The ancient wisdom is that health is a balance, harmony and synthesis of the various features of the self. Extreme reactions are thus the very antithesis of a balanced approach to life. They lead not only to a denial or repression of various features of the self but to tension between what become warring forces rather than complementary tendencies. This tension is experienced not only within the individual concerned but by others in their social networks. Thus the woman whose guide pointed her towards healing others as a means of continuing her self-development thought this required her to give up her very well-paid job. Not only did this become a source of stress for her, because she derived great enjoyment and satisfaction from it as well as a luxurious lifestyle, but for those around her, notably her family, who would suffer the 'knock-on' effect of her loss of income and the prospect of a martyr in their midst. However, when confronted with the black-white nature of her reaction this woman was able to reconcile the two tendencies within her: she was able to care for herself and her family *and* for others, and thus achieve a compromise whereby she continued in her job but gave healing at other times.

The inner guide may give advice or guidance that the person does not necessarily wish to 'hear' but which, when acted on, proves to be of value. For those who are able to employ it as an ally and take heed of its intelligence it can be a transforming principle, and one which has great practical application. Not only the sick but the healthy can use it in all kinds of ways. It is, for example, a shrewd guide to business affairs and the everyday management of one's life. If in doubt about the wisdom of a course of action, why not consult the inner guide?

One practical application which I have found particularly useful is to draw upon the inner guide as an aid to those who suffer severe nightmares. By summoning their inner guide such individuals are usually able to 'relive' their ordeal with full protection, and therefore to examine its content for meaning which otherwise would have proved impossible because of their fear. Having thus divined the significance of the dream it rarely returns, its 'message' having been delivered to the conscious mind and, hopefully, acted upon.

It is, however, important to recognise that the Inner Guide exercise may conjure unpleasant images. Jung described the less attractive or negative aspect of the self as the 'shadow'. This needs to be integrated with the rest of the self and should therefore be fully acknowledged and accepted. Nevertheless this is best achieved with the support of one's inner resources or guide and so negative or unpleasant features of the self which emerge in this exercise should be dismissed until the inner guide has been contacted and integrated. This can then be used as an aid in confronting the shadowy aspects of self, much as is described above in relation to the unpleasant features of dreams and nightmares. For this reason the exercise instructions specify that any image which evokes unpleasant or threatening responses should be dismissed.

10

DIRECTING SUBTLE ENERGIES

Life flows on within you, and without you.
George Harrison

The previous exercise was concerned with mobilising psychic energies in support of healing. Traditional approaches to healing throughout the world since antiquity share a belief in the existence of subtle energies, health being viewed as the mobilisation and balancing of these energies, and illness as their stagnation or disruption.

Throughout the ancient world these energies were conceived not as some kind of substance or thing, but as continuous movement or change, all phenomena – light, sound, heat, colour, thought, emotion and material bodies – being simply movement in a particular state of vibration.

Such a view, for so long regarded as incompatible with Western scientific knowledge, is now widely acknowledged to be fully consistent with the theories and findings of modern physics, which suggests that in the final analysis all matter, including the human body, is nothing but energy in constant transformation. When this is recognised it becomes easier to understand how subtle energetic influences, including the psychological and emotional, can have a direct influence on physical or material entities, and vice versa.

Unfortunately insufficient people do realise this, and even within the scientific community, especially the medical fraternity, there is frequently a reluctance to accept the implications of recent scientific discovery, much less acknowledge that the principles have been understood and applied in healing practices throughout the world for thousands of years. However, there seems to be little doubt that this is in fact the case.

176

Energy centres of the body: the chakra system

In the various traditions of the ancient world one encounters time and again the concept of subtle energies distributed through the human body by a number of energy centres, which are typically depicted as three-dimensional pulsating wheels or vortices. Clairvoyants or seers through the ages have described these as being like cones, trumpets, or the flowers of the convolvulus (bindweed), which, according to the direction in which they spin, either draw energies into or direct them out of the body, enervating or depleting its vitality.

These centres are located not in the physical body but in a second, immaterial counterpart which envelopes it. Known as the Ka by the Ancient Egyptians and variously as the astral or etheric body, or double, in Western traditions, it is generally synonymous with the concept of spirit. This spiritual body is thought to act like a prism, refracting energy in the form of light into seven streams which correspond with the frequency bands of the electro-magnetic spectrum. Each band is then drawn to a different energy centre whose vibrations are of the same frequency, from where it is distributed throughout the body. Accordingly each centre is believed to vibrate at a characteristic frequency. Its energy pattern is therefore held to be predominantly of a certain colour, and associated with a musical note, certain elements, symbolic forms and planetary influences whose vibrations correspond with this frequency. Although some details vary, these centres have been variously described and depicted in the traditions of Native Northern and Central Americans and the peoples of Tibet, India and the Far East. Evidence that they have long been known in the West comes from their depiction on the monuments of Ancient Egypt, from the ancient rituals of Freemasonry and other occult traditions, and the writings of European mystics.

Nevertheless they were first written about in English only in the early years of this century, when the Sanskrit term *chakra*, meaning wheel, was retained. Despite some variation in their number and position, there is broad agreement that there are seven principal chakras, situated at the base of the

177

spine, just below and above the navel, adjacent to the heart, at the throat, between the eyebrows, and at the top of the head.

In recent times chakras have been identified with the location and function of the glands of the endocrine system, namely and gonads, liver, adrenals, thymus, thyroid, pineal and pituitary respectively. The slightest imbalance of energy in any of these chakras is considered to influence the corresponding gland, giving rise to fluctuations in hormones, which, being secreted directly into the blood stream, create immediate changes in mood, appearance, tension, respiration, digestion, intelligence and intuition, thereby effecting the entire organism. The various traditions hold that by understanding the characteristic function, associated colour, sound, element, mineral and symbolic form associated with each chakra, their energies can be regulated and balanced. This belief forms the basis of most ancient forms of healing, including the various practices of Ancient Egypt and Greece, where colour and sound were extensively used in treatment; those of traditional Indian, Tibetan, Chinese and Japanese medicine, including systems of exercise such as yoga, T'ai Chi and Aikido which promote the flow of energy through the centres; and the universal use of 'power' objects such as crystals and stones by shamans and witchdoctors.

The principal features of the chakra system do vary slightly from tradition to tradition, but those aspects relevant to healing can be summarised as below:

The first, root or base chakra, located at the base of the spine, is considered to be concerned with basic existence and survival, influencing sexual activity and regulating creativity in the widest sense. It affects the sex glands, ovaries and testes and is responsible for sex-drive, reproduction and secondary sex characteristics. This procreative energy may be transformed and expressed in all forms of creative activity, personal growth, health and healing.

The second chakra, located midway between the pubic bone and the naval, is considered in traditional systems to be the centre of sexual activity but in the West is associated with the spleen, liver and pancreas, glands which influence the metabolism, digestion, detoxification, immunity to disease, and fluid and sugar balance within the body. It is therefore associated with cleansing, purification and health, and with 'gut feelings' or strong, basic emotions or instincts.

The third, or solar plexus chakra, situated just above the navel, is considered to be the centre of power and emotion, influencing the adrenal glands, which profoundly affect the sympathetic nervous system and thereby heartbeat, digestion, circulation, mood and muscle function. It is implicated in stress disorders characterised by excessive use of adrenalin, notably ulcers, nervous disorders and chronic fatigue.

The fourth, or heart chakra, situated in the centre of the chest, is considered to be the source of love and compassion, and the seat of unconditional love. On a physical level it is thought to influence the thymus gland situated just behind the breast bone, the main function of which in adults is the proper utilisation of the amino-competence factor, which helps promote immunity to disease.

The fifth, or throat chakra is concerned with creativity and self-expression. It is thought to relate to the functioning of the thyroid gland, which affects metabolism, the musculature and control of body temperature.

The sixth chakra, located just above and between the eyebrows, is traditionally referred to as the 'third eye' and described as the seat of ecstasy, clairvoyance, heightened intuition and paranormal powers. It is associated with the pineal gland, which is now thought to have a significant role in the production of visual imagery and unconscious processes.

The crown chakra, located in the centre of the upper skull, is regarded as the seat of cosmic consciousness or enlightenment, and held to be beyond thought, name or rational experience. More recently it has been associated with the pituitary or 'master' gland of the body, but traditionally it is associated with pure being and the symbolic form of the thousand-petalled lotus-flower, which has its roots in the dense energies at the base of the spine, its stem in water – that is, the emotional energies of the torso – and its blossom untouched by water and fully opened to the energy of the sun. When fully opened it represents the integrated functioning of the individual at all levels, physical, psychological and spiritual.

The chakras, rather than regulating purely physical well-being, are also concerned with psychological and spiritual functioning and thus with the totality of body, mind and spirit. Accordingly, the chakra system provides the impetus for the regulated, balanced flow of energy throughout the whole organism, which is equivalent with health.

The aura

According to the various traditions, each of these centres emits energy which reflects its state of functioning, and forms a distinct band of a hazy emanation which extends around the body for some distance. Normally invisible, this radiant energy field is described by seers or those with super-sensitive sight as a shimmering oval, comprising a mass of fine, luminescent fibres or rays. Although widely referred to as the aura, this phenomenon was described in early Christian times as the halo, which in later Renaissance and medieval art was commonly depicted as confined to the head region of the body. All objects, living or not, are traditionally believed to be completely enveloped in an individual aura, which acts as a medium for the interplay of other energies present in the immediate environment, and collectively to create a common auric or etheric realm of energy.

The appearance, shape and size of the individual aura are considered to reveal the overall state of functioning of the form it envelops. In the human being the aura is the sum total of the energy given off by the chakras. Well-being depends on the proper reception and distribution of energies by these centres and therefore on harmony and balance. When each is operating in a balanced, harmonious manner the colour emanating from it should be clear and pale, indicating that its energy transmission is pure and subtle. Accordingly the presence of darker, denser colour emanations, manifesting in the aura as patches or blotches, is an indication that the relevant chakra is not functioning properly and the energy not being transmitted effectively. Moreover, as the etheric or spiritual body is the blueprint of the physical body, controlling and affecting what occurs there, energy imbalance is thought to be indicated in the aura before it manifests in the physical body. The aura can, therefore, be used for diagnosis.

The bands of the aura correspond with the functioning and principal colour of each chakra. According to most systems, the first band, emanating from the base chakra, is reddish in colour, and reflects the overall physical vitality of the body. The second band, emanating from the second chakra, is associated with 'gut feelings', reflects emotions, and is predominantly orange in colour. The third band, emanating from the solar plexus, reflects lower mental functions based on the intellect and objective, factual 'knowledge', and is yellow. The fourth band, emanating from the heart, corresponds with the higher mental abilities, intuition and inspiration, and is green. The fifth band, emanating from the throat chakra, is traditionally regarded as reflecting the progression of the soul or spirit through successive incarnations, and therefore the way the self has been expressed throughout its development. It is sky-blue. The sixth band of the aura, which is dark blue, emanates from the third eye and reflects spiritual awareness. The seventh band, emanating from the crown chakra, and purple in colour, reflects cosmic awareness or transcendence.

In its totality, therefore, the aura reveals the individual's state of physical health, characteristic emotional disposition and tendencies, abilities, aptitudes, attitudes, past problems and spiritual development.

Throughout history and in all cultures, sensitives or seers have reported sensing or objectively seeing these bands, and have often represented them in sketches or paintings, using them as a basis for diagnosis and treatment, and for counselling on personal, interpersonal and transpersonal development.

Research by a British physician, Sheila Karagulla, suggests that many orthodox medical practitioners have the ability to diagnose illness in this way, and such abilities are currently under investigation in the USA. Those whose abilities are highly developed claim that sensitivity to auras can be trained, and there are various exercises that are used for training auric sight. Arguably, however, everyone already has a certain degree of sensitivity to auras, as we typically describe others in energy and colour images as brilliant, shining, sparkling, radiant, dim, dull, green, blue, yellow or in the pink. Although it is easy to dismiss these expressions as merely colourful speech, there is nevertheless objective evidence for the existence of the aura since the electromagnetic forcefield around the person is measurable and visible by various means such as Kilner screens and Kirlian photography.

Taken as a whole, these notions of subtle energies provide an integrative framework for a great number of approaches to healing, including traditional Indian, Tibetan, Chinese and Japanese systems of medicine.

Indian and Tibetan medicine

From their origins in ancient times Indian and Tibetan systems of healing have been directed to the promotion of health, as opposed simply to the treatment of disease, by achieving the flow and balance of energies within the person. Yoga, although widely regarded in the West as no more than a series of physical exercises, is a complete self-help health programme that embraces the whole person in his physical, psychological and spiritual aspects. It therefore takes many forms, the most widely known in the West being *hatha* yoga, which focuses on promoting maximum efficiency of the vital energies through physical exercise and breathing. However, this is merely a preparation for other forms of yoga that employ meditation and imagery, their aim being transcendence, or union with Ultimate Reality, the totality of creation. One widespread meditative form, *mantra* yoga, which is based on ancient knowledge of sound vibrations, is directed to the promotion of wholeness or health by the rhythmical repetition of certain sounds.

Chinese and Japanese medicine

Traditional Chinese and Japanese medicine is based on similar concepts of energy – or *chi* – which is considered to circulate the body along various pathways or meridians, each of which is associated with various bodily functions and organs. Illness is regarded as a breakdown in this process and consequent imbalance of energy flow. Treatment therefore focuses on the normalisation of energy flow. This is achieved by stimulating various sensitive points, known as acupuncture points in China and *tsubo* in Japan, that are believed to exert influence on the body organs related to the meridian on which the point lies. In Chinese medicine different forms of treatment are applied to these sites, the most widely known in the West being acupuncture, in which fine needles are inserted into the points and stimulated manually or electrically. Other methods include acupressure, or the application of manual pressure at these points, and moxibustion, the supplementation of energy at the site by igniting a small cone of dried plant leaves.

Acupuncture is also widely used in Japanese medicine, as is Shiatsu or finger pressure, which is analogous to acupressure. Other treatments employing various degrees of touch are also used, including Do-in, the self-stimulation of certain body areas by friction, pressure, percussion and breathing techniques; Anma, which uses massage, kneading and stretching of tissue; and Reiki, a form of laying-on-hands which involves the channelling and balancing of energies.

However, as in other Eastern traditions, the focus of Chinese and Japanese medicine is on prevention rather than cure, so much so that traditional doctors were paid only while their patients remained in good health. Balanced energy flow throughout the body is also promoted in the series of breathing and movement exercises known as T'ai Chi. A similar system of exercises, Aikido, is widely employed by the Japanese.

Reflexology, zone therapy and metamorphic technique, which are becoming increasingly widespread in the West, derive from similar principles, and their growing popularity is an indication that the efficacy of some of the healing methods disregarded in the West until relatively recently is being recognised. Modern research suggests that acupuncture, which is now widely available in general hospitals, produces the natural pain-killer endorphin and, in addition, modifies the body's perception of pain through the release of other neuro-chemicals. When used as an anaesthetic during surgical operations it has been found to have fewer side-effects than conventional anaesthetics, and when used during Caesarian section it produces less blood loss, faster post-operative recovery with fewer complications, and reduces the need for pain-killers. Verification of the existence and functions of meridians and chakras, and their integration, has been provided by extensive research in Japan over a period of some thirty years. Devices for recording and measuring the flow of subtle energies have been developed, and standardised data has been obtained for the normal range of functioning during good health and patterns of ill health from many thousands of subjects. Experimental investigations of the psycho-physiology of the integrated chakra-meridian system in the West also confirm the claims of traditional medicine about the functions of these subtle energies (Roney-Dougal, 1989; Young, 1990).

Homeopathic medicine

Homeopathic medicine has a similar conceptual basis to acupuncture. Its originator, Dr Samuel Hahnemann, claimed that certain basic vibrational patterns of disease, originating in the aura, set up patterns in the individual's mind/body system which spread their influence through all that person's energies. The organism reacts to this imbalance in its energies by attempting to restore balance, and in so doing produces the symptoms and signs that the patient feels and the doctor observes.

Unlike the ordinary physician, the homeopathic practitioner does not consider the symptoms to be the illness *per se*, but simply the body's reactions to the state of imbalance. They are thus an indicator of the extent of the imbalance and how profoundly the organism is affected by it, and can be used to determine treatment appropriate to restoring balance and health.

Homeopathic treatments work by matching minute doses of various natural remedies of different vibrational characters with different imbalances in the body, thereby restoring harmony to its energy patterns. They utilise the principle of resonance, or 'like cures like', applying remedies that subject the organism to a disturbance of the same frequency as that of the symptoms. This effectively shakes up the body's energies and moves them into a more harmonious arrangement.

Homeopathic medicine is widely available in Britain, having been available through the National Health Service since 1977. There are many homeopathic physicians within orthodox medicine, and several homeopathic hospitals. Its most distinguished patrons in Britain are the Royal Family, who employ homeopathic remedies in the maintenance of their health and that of their animals. Indeed, homeopathy is increasingly being practised and researched within the field of veterinary medicine, and several papers on the subject were presented at the 1990 Conference of the British Small Animals Veterinary Association.

Traditionally it has been recognised that insight into the subtle energies of the body and the functioning of its energy centres can be facilitated through imagery, which provides a means of consciously accessing what is essentially unconscious, non-verbal information. Energy imagery is therefore increasingly playing a role in psychological approaches to healing, reflecting once again a return to the shamanic origins of the healing arts.

Exercise 10
Sensing subtle energies through imagery

Imagine you are sitting with eyes closed directly under a warm sun that is progressively soothing aches, pains and tensions from your mind and body.

When you feel relaxed and at ease, imagine that you momentarily glance up at the sun. You see light streaming from it, and the rays appear to form a pyramid or cone which envelops you on all sides, flooding you with soothing, protective warmth. Take some time to experience this.

Having done so, imagine that you glance up at the sun again. The sun's rays now appear to be like streams of white rain – a waterfall of light – raining gently down upon you. This light rain passes through the pores of your skin on the crown of your head. Located within, there is a wheel which distributes the light throughout the top of your head.

Take note of its size and construction, its colour, the direction and quality of its movement, and how well it is distributing the light. Then follow the light as it is distributed downwards through your head to a second wheel situated between your eyebrows.

Again notice every detail of that wheel, then follow the light downwards as it is distributed to a third wheel situated in the centre of your throat. Pay careful attention to all the features of the wheel before following the light as it is distributed down through your body to a fourth wheel situated over your breast bone in the centre of your chest.

Observe what is happening there before following the light as it is distributed downwards through your body to a fifth wheel situated about two inches above your navel. Note in as much detail as possible the characteristics of this wheel and its mode of action before again following the light downwards to a wheel situated some two inches below the navel.

Once again pay careful attention to all the features of the wheel and its movement before following the light as it is distributed downwards to a wheel situated over the pubic bone.

Having observed this wheel in detail, look upwards at the column of wheels above. Note how they compare with each other; whether they are similar in size, lying in the same plane, moving in the same direction and at the same speed. Observe how well aligned and co-ordinated they are, and whether or not the light flows smoothly and easily between them. Try and regulate them so that the flow of light from one to the other is smooth, easy and harmonious.

Having done so, bring your attention back to the base of your spine, where a pool of liquid light is forming. Imagine this seeping out from the base of your spine so that you are sitting at the centre of a growing pool of light, which is extending away from you in a series of concentric circles. Notice the colours of each of these bands of light, and whether they are pale, dark, dense or patchy. Try and see where in your body any dark blotches or patches of colour are coming from and try to clear them so that the pool is pale, transparent and luminescent.

Imagine this pool of light spreading out to join the pools of light surrounding other people and things, initially those nearest to you, progressing to those further and further away, so that you see yourself, all people and things floating in an endless sea, each being like a small ripple or wave on its vast surface.

Be aware that all things are interconnected, and that by your actions you affect everything else, just as you are affected by *their* actions. Now allow this image to fade. Bring your attention gradually back to your body so that once again you imagine yourself sitting within a radiant cone or pyramid of protective light. Then gradually allow yourself to return to normal, and take a few minutes to record your experience.

Commentary

In order to avoid creating expectations, I normally give no introduction to this exercise in my workshops. The majority of those participating have little or no knowledge of chakras or auras, and even those who do are generally not sufficiently well versed in their details and subtleties to correlate their own imagery with the physical, psychological and spiritual influences attributed to chakras and auras in traditional theory. Nevertheless, the correspondence between them is striking and consistent, and sufficient to persuade those who might otherwise have doubts as to their validity.

People generally have little difficulty in visualising the various energy wheels of the body, although they may find that some are missing or difficult to picture in detail. They may find themselves moving in synchrony with the wheels, and circular movement or swaying is frequently perceptible to observers.

Most people find that their wheels differ in size and velocity, with each wheel becoming progressively larger and moving more slowly. This in itself is of interest because according to traditional wisdom the vibrations of each chakra become progressively more dense, heavy and lower in frequency down the length of the spine.

The wheels often appear to tilt in various directions or to lie in different planes – an arrangement which may or may not impede the flow of light. Similarly, the direction of movement may vary from one wheel to another. The quality of movement tends to vary considerably from person to person, and within a person from one wheel to another. Thus some wheels seem immobile, stuck or slow, others rapid, erratic or eccentric, while a few do not revolve or rotate but swing in the manner of a pendulum.

187

Structurally the wheels are very variable, some appearing to the individuals concerned as brittle, fragile, delicate, weak or faulty, and others as strong, durable and powerful. They may be made of glass, crystal, plastic, rubber, various metals, wood, cardboard or light, and appear in the form of cogs and clock-wheels, water-wheels, Ferris wheels, Catherine wheels or paddle-boat wheels – indeed, wheels of every conceivable kind and construction. Similarly the light may vary in quality and character. Whereas in some cases it is clear and fluid, rather like water, in others it is thick, dense and sticky, like tar, glue or sludge. It may also be variable in colour. One woman saw her crown chakra as a water-wheel with deep buckets, converting the light into house-bricks, which could not be distributed by the other wheels, and so piled up within her. Some are highly efficient, while others are considerably less so. Accordingly, while some wheels seem flooded or overwhelmed with light, others do not receive or distribute any.

As people scan their wheels they are usually able to identify those that are impeding the free flow of light throughout their system, and they may also be able to remedy the situation, by imagining slowing or speeding certain wheels, effecting repairs or making other modifications. This is to be encouraged, because, as with the immune system imagery, there are indications that it has beneficial effects.

Indeed, many traditional meditations are directed towards influencing chakra function through imagery in a similar way. As has already been noted, mantra meditations involve the silent repetition of sounds that correspond with the characteristic vibrational pattern of certain chakras in an attempt to influence their functioning, and many very ancient meditations involve vizualisation of symbolic forms and colours for similar purposes.

Although participants are directed to observe any colour associated with each wheel, this appears not to be a salient factor for many people. However, this is not so in respect of the pool of light. Colour emerges very clearly as a significant feature for most people, and once again the character and quality of the colour is extremely variable. In some cases the pool of light is virtually colourless, pale and translucent.

Others describe it as dark and dense, thick and static with the appearance of diesel-oil or tar. For some, one colour predominates, again of varying quality, while for others a number of colours are identifiable.

The distribution of colour is also very variable, some seeing only slight traces or edges of colour, others noting distinct colour bands, patches or blotches.

However, the colours noted tend to correspond with anomalies in the relevant wheels. Thus a person with a predominantly bright blue pool of water typically describes 'problems' in relation to the wheel imagined at her throat, while someone with significant amounts of red in her pool usually reports difficulty with her base wheel.

In some groups where there have been persons present who possess auric vision – the ability to perceive auras objectively or heightened sensitivity to them – they have described the same colours surrounding individual group members as those persons have themselves subjectively perceived around themselves during the exercise. However, it is not necessary to possess clairvoyant abilities to achieve this. When asked to do so, most group members accurately describe the predominant colours they sense around those people adjacent to them, inasmuch as their perception corresponds with the subjective perception of the individuals in question and of others. When doing this, some people recognise that they can detect quite definite sensations emanating from others of which they were previously unaware, and it is precisely this awareness that is possessed and cultivated by shamans, and trained in would-be healers.

The reasons for cultivating this awareness become more clear when it is realised that the subjectively perceived or intuited colours not only correspond to the features of relevant wheels as perceived by the individuals, but also relate to the characteristic dis-ease of that person. Missing, weak, faulty or erratic wheels often correspond with dysfunctions of the relevant endocrine glands. A typical example would be the person who describes the wheel in his throat as static or sluggish and also substantial patches of blue light in the 'pool' of his aura, only to reveal subsequently that he has a dysfunctional thyroid. One young woman with a serious pituitary disorder found the wheel at the crown of her head hardly moving at all, with serious implications for all the other wheels in her system. Another young woman, who subsequently reported suffering from a serious auto-immune condition, described her heart chakra as revolving so rapidly it seemed totally out of control and about to disintegrate. Frequently people with immuno-deficient conditions and cancer experience 'difficulties' with this chakra, whereas those who suffer stress-related conditions or neuroses encounter problems in the solar plexus, usually in relation to disproportionately large or over-active wheels. Stomach and digestive problems may be associated with this chakra, but more so with the second chakra, and genito-urinary problems with the first. Frequently women who experience fertility problems or repeated miscarriages perceive anomalies in the base chakra.

Nevertheless, it has to be emphasised that each chakra relates to functioning on a number of different levels, and so imaginery wheels do not necessarily relate to physical functioning. A person who discovers certain quirks in a given wheel should not automatically assume they are ill, or likely to be. They should, however, consider the whole range of functioning associated with that centre and address themselves to the implications of possible energy imbalance in this area. An example of this is provided by a woman who was very depressed following a miscarriage. From what has been described it may come as no great surprise that she described a good deal of red in her aura image. However, subsequent examination revealed that her real concern was with the more general blockage of her creative potentials. She had given up a highly stimulating and creative job in order to start the family both she and her husband wanted, but her experience of motherhood following the birth of her first child was one of disappointment. She found herself bored and unstimulated, and motherhood 'difficult'. Thus the loss of her second baby gave her a justification for being depressed about a far more general lack of productivity. Another woman who reported concern over her base chakra imagery indicated that her desire for more children was thwarted by a number of personal and social factors, which not only left her frustrated, but also unable to channel her creativity in other ways.

Emotional and intellectual blockages may be highlighted by the imagery. Perhaps the most commonly encountered is the difficulty many women have in relation to the throat chakra. This does not suggest that women are necessarily predisposed to thyroid problems, but rather that many of them have problems of self-expression, especially in relation to the expression of certain emotions and potentials, which reflects the social conditioning and status of women rather more than their level of thyroxine. Nevertheless the relationship between physical and psychological or spiritual disorders cannot be overlooked. Energy blockages or excess energy flow are likely to manifest at both the physical and psychological levels, and thus a fundamental principle of all traditional healing is that both domains have to be addressed simultaneously.

11

LISTENING TO THE WISDOM
OF THE BODY

The light is within thee; let the light shine.
Matthew 5:16

The significance of the exercise in the previous chapter lies in the 'light' it can shed on the distribution and utilisation of subtle energies in the body. Traditional forms of healing recognise that, when these energies cannot flow freely in the body, this sets up over time a chronic imbalance in tissues and organs that allows infection or functional disorder to become established. It also produces neurotic responses that are shown behaviourally, and certain characteristic patterns of muscular expression and posture.

In recent times such a view has been propounded by the psychotherapist Wilhelm Reich, and developed by him and others into a comprehensive diagnostic and therapeutic system.

Reich's theory is that emotional and psychological ways of relating to the world are reflected physically in the body, and vice versa. He thus viewed the organism as a unified whole that reacts as a totality to various influences rather than solely mentally or physically. Accordingly, neurotic responses are indicated in a person's entire behaviour, the neurotic being literally rigid, tense and 'uptight'. Reich therefore took the view that the body and the mind should be addressed simultaneously, and in so doing laid the foundations for a psychosomatic psychology and treatments which, in a quite literal sense, address the *psyche* (mind/soul) by way of the body, or *soma*.

His therapy was directed towards identifying and eliminating characteristic muscular patterns, or character structures, which have developed as defensive responses, or 'armouring', in response to trauma or stress.

He described seven rings of character structure, or tension resulting from muscle armouring, at right angles to the main axis of the body:

1 eyes, forehead, scalp;
2 mouth, chin, jaw;
3 neck, shoulders;
4 thorax, heart, lungs, arms;
5 diaphragm;
6 abdomen, lower back;
7 pelvis.

When worked upon physically through a combination of breathing exercises and massage, these areas release blocked energy at both physical and psychological levels, re-establishing its natural flow and normalising physical and psychological functions.

These seven rings correspond very strikingly with the traditional chakra areas, and David Boadella, a psychotherapist who has further developed Reich's work, suggests that it may therefore be appropriate to regard the principal character structures of Reich's theory as primary functional disturbances of these energy centres. He identifies character patterns in relation to the chakras as follows:

1 *Root chakra* The primary function of this is grounding, commitment to the body and the will to survive. Where well developed, these energies manifest as a sense of independence and personal power. Where dysfunctional, they manifest as tendencies to over-groundedness, fear of dependence, or as insecurity and fear of independence. The character patterns associated with this chakra thus express a polarity between rigidity and helplessness, control and collapse.

2 *Hara* The primary function of this, the second chakra, is charge or sexuality. Dysfunction will show as over or under charge: that is, as hypersexuality – casual contact

193

and difficulty in achieving satisfactory sexual relations; or as hyposexuality – impotence, frigidity and sexual anaesthesia through inability to achieve satisfactory contact.

3 *Solar plexus* This chakra relates primarily to power and mastery, and thus to boundaries, anger and anxiety. Basic conflicts will be expressed in identification with power, domination and anger, or submission and anxiety, rather than blending and co-operation.

4 *Heart* Associated with compassion, love, the formation of strong relationships and bonding, dysfunction manifests here in overbonded, addictive and stifling patterns in relationships, or, alternatively, in underbonding expressed in superficial or transitory relationships, perhaps with a degree of indifference; or as total withdrawal from relationships.

5 *Throat* The primary function of this chakra is communication, notably the expression of the heart via the voice. Dysfunction is reflected in distortions of language, in introjection – swallowing whole the views of others without discrimination; in rejection of one's own feelings; and in projection – believing others to have attributes one is unwilling to ascribe to oneself. Guilt and shame are strongly implicated when this centre is blocked.

6 *Brow* The function of this chakra is vision and contemplation – looking out and seeing in – and therefore the ability to see oneself and others clearly. It is related to imagination and insight. Dysfunction shows in obsession, the narrowing of vision to a single focus, and loss of imagination and insight; and at the other extreme, in feelings of possession or being invaded by others, and excessive telepathic openness.

7 *Crown* This chakra is associated with openness to something greater than the self. Dysfunction can lead to messianic inflation and feelings of omnipotence; or to nihilistic deflation, existential depression, fear of death and despair at the ultimate meaninglessness of life. Being related to the contact between inner and outer space, these disorders relate to 'spacing out' and fear of extinction or being 'outspaced'.

The character patterns associated with the chakras as detailed by Boadella can thus be summarised:

Crown   – spacing
Brow   – facing
Throat   – sounding
Heart   – bonding
Solar Plexus – bounding
Hara   – centring
Root   – grounding

It is therefore possible to use the chakras in the diagnosis of both psychological and physical dysfunction.

The question is, however, if these insights are diagnostically valid and reliable, as seems to be suggested by recent scientific research (Roney-Dougal, 1989; Young, 1990), what kinds of treatments are appropriate to the restoration of normal functioning and balance?

Healing through bodywork

A number of bodywork or 'bioenergetic' approaches have been developed in the Reichian tradition with the common aim of relaxing the body and releasing the energy held in by various muscle groups. These therapies involve working directly on the body to unblock and regulate energy flow by massage and various forms of manipulation. However, as they invariably involve the intervention and assistance of others, they do not constitute self-healing. Certain forms of bodywork can be self-administered, as is the case with Japanese Do-in, acupressure, and Shiatsu, which can be applied to accessible areas. Reflexology can be applied just as effectively to the hands and ears, which are more amenable to self-manipulation, as to the feet, which are more commonly the locus of treatment.

Systems of exercise such as hatha yoga, T'ai Chi and Aikido may be regarded as self-help, preventative strategies which promote the flow of energy in the body and obviate the need for a good deal of corrective treatment.

A similar kind of self-awareness is demanded by the

Alexander Technique and the Feldenkrais Method. The former is not a set of exercises as such, but a training of an individual's self-awareness in how certain activities are accomplished, with the aim of improving postural and muscular activity. The Feldenkrais Method is similarly concerned with developing the full efficiency and functioning of the body, and, in focusing on gradual training of bodily awareness and sensitivity, incorporates elements of the Alexander Technique and martial arts disciplines. It differs from the Alexander Technique in its emphasis on body motion rather than posture, and as such is similar to T'ai Chi.

There are, of course, ways other than these primarily physical methods for dealing with physical imbalance. Most traditional forms of healing recognise that conscious mental processes can influence bodily functioning, and that meditation or intentional, intense concentration on the chakras can stimulate relevant energies. The ancients recognised what modern brain sciences are only just beginning to learn, which is that imagery is the supreme mediator between the mental and physical realms, transforming the energies from one to the other. Accordingly, visualisation of shapes, symbols or colours is sufficient to stimulate energy centres of similar vibrational character within the body, enabling restoration of their normal pattern of functioning.

Colour therapy

The ancients understood that colour, whether in the physical form of light and pigment or the psychic form of imagery, influences the subtle energies of the body, and that meditation on colour, or its visualisation, could be as effective in treatment as direct exposure to colour. The Ancient Egyptians and Greeks, like traditional healers in most cultures, used coloured salves in treatment, coloured stones and crystals, and sanctuaries painted in various shades.

Traditionally red is associated with heat – both physical heat such as fire and 'heated' emotions – and expressed by inflammation and fever, whereas blue is identified with ice and snow, and associated with coolness and sedation.

Modern research supports these notions, demonstrating

that plants grown under red glass grow more quickly than usual, while those grown under blue glass grow much more slowly. Animals reared under red lights also grow more quickly than normal, while those kept under blue light grow denser coats.

The subtle effects of light on humans are only now becoming more fully appreciated as a result of extensive research in this area (Wood, 1987; Gimbel, 1978; Wilson and Bek, 1987; Birren, 1978). Exposure to coloured light has clear psycho-physiological effects. Red light stimulates both body and mind, raising blood pressure, increasing respiration and heartbeat, and arousing powerful emotions such as anger and aggression. Blue light has the opposite effect in that it calms and sedates, and has very marked healing properties. It is now widely used in healing injured tissue and preventing formation of scar tissue, and in the treatment of cancers, non-malignant tumours, and skin and lung conditions. In the USA, ultraviolet light is now the standard treatment for psoriasis and other skin conditions, and blue light has also replaced blood transfusions for babies born with potentially fatal neonatal jaundice. Early in 1990 scientists reported to the annual conference of the American Association of the Advancement of Science on the successful use of blue light in the treatment of a wide variety of ailments including alcoholism, anorexia nervosa, loss of sex drive and depression. Indeed, studies have confirmed the ancient wisdom concerning the effects of colour on the emotions. Various studies have shown that pink has a soporific and tranquillising effect and suppresses hostile, aggressive and anxious behaviour, which is interesting given its traditional association with femininity in Western culture. Its sedative and muscle-relaxing effects are now being exploited in the decoration of geriatric and adolescent units, family therapy clinics, prisons and reformatories, and in business settings. By comparison, yellow light has a highly stimulating effect, and a correlation has been noted between the high incidence of street crime and the use of sodium yellow street-lighting.

These effects are not confined to sighted persons but are also demonstrable in the blind. Indeed, it is well-established that colour need not be visually perceived for it to have

197

definite psychological and physiological effects. Moreover, colours can be distinguished by blind, colour-blind and blindfold subjects. This phenomenon, variously referred to as 'eyeless sight', dermo-optic vision or bio-introscopy, has been the subject of research since the 1920s when it was first established that blindfold persons could recognise both colours and shapes with their forehead (the traditional site of the so-called 'third eye'), and could precisely describe colours and shapes presented under glass which prevented any contact with them. Research in Russia has found that the ability to identify colour via the fingertips is not as exceptional as had previously been thought, and that subjects can be trained to recognise colour in this way in 20–30 minutes (Ivanov, 1965). Blind people develop this sensitivity even more quickly. Some subjects can distinguish colours correctly without touch when their fingers are 20–80 centimetres above colour cards, and typically they describe experiencing sensations varying from needle pricks to faint breezes, depending on the colour.

Initial explanations of the phenomenon focused on structural differences in dyeing substances, but this failed to explain how colour could be distinguished under glass or tracing paper, or how different-coloured light beams could be discriminated. Thermal differences were eliminated by systematically heating and cooling the cards, even though subjects did not report temperature differences as the basis of their discrimination. The suggestion that eyeless sight is in some way electrical is confounded by the fact that subjects are still able to detect colours presented under aluminium foil, brass or copper plates.

So, despite considerable research, the phenomenon remains something of an enigma, although there is little doubt that colour is experienced subjectively and qualitatively as well as objectively.

Colour researchers have suggested that, since mental activities, emotional reactions and the metabolic system are linked, colours stimulate both psychological and physical processes by chemical changes so subtle that they cannot be detected by conventional recording devices. Certainly it has long been held that the varying electro-magnetic properties of colour affect the endocrine system, notably the pituitary and pineal glands, thereby influencing mood at all times, usually subtly, but sometimes quite dramatically.

Support for such a claim is provided by research into the hormone melatonin, which is produced by the pineal gland and is now known to be the crucial chemical pathway by which animals respond to light, and thus the means by which they synchronise their bodily functioning with diurnal, lunar and seasonal variations (Roney-Dougal, 1989).

When it is dark, melatonin output increases and this has a depressive effect which is reversed when it is light and melatonin production drops. As the pineal gland has connections with all the other glands of the endocrine system, melatonin has numerous effects within the body, most notably on reproductive processes, which are particularly influenced by fluctuation in the output of this hormone, and thus by changes in light. This factor has been recognised for countless generations by livestock breeders, especially race-horse breeders, who make extensive use of artificial light in the regulation of breeding programmes.

The effects of melatonin are well established in animals and are also discernible in humans. Women with ovulation problems, or anorexia nervosa, a characteristic feature of which is amenorrhea or absence of menstruation, have been found to have very high levels of melatonin, as do men with low sperm count and people suffering from SAD, or Seasonal Affective Depression, which usually occurs during winter. Depression appears to be closely linked with melatonin levels and to show rapid improvement in response to light therapy, exposure either to natural sunlight or full-spectrum lamps.

These recent discoveries lend support to the theories of Max Lüscher, a former professor of psychology at the University of Basle. Over half a century ago he claimed that colour preferences are an indication of states of mind or glandular imbalance, or both, and can be used as the basis for physical and psychological diagnosis. His theory, which forms the basis of the Luscher Colour Test, is that the significance of colour for humans originates in our early history when our behaviour was governed by night and day. He claimed that the colours of these two environments, dark blue and yellow, are associated with differences in metabolic rate and glandular secretions appropriate to the energies required for night-time sleep and day-time activity such as foraging and hunting, and that other autonomic responses are associated with different colours.

Therapies that employ colour, whether as light, pigments or mental imagery, are consistent with the view that, by applying colour vibrations to relevant chakras, endocrine and related functions can be stimulated. In some cases therapists diagnose the appropriate colours by working with the aura, either sensing or seeing imbalances clairvoyantly. Colour can then be applied physically, or psychically by the healer visualising colour being directed to the appropriate site. Colour visualisation can also be employed to good effect in self-healing, as is indicated by Cleary (1988), who describes its effects on a twelve-year-old girl dying of cancer.

Because of its possible significance as a cue to dysfunction, colour that presents in association with imagery should always be noted. Persistent colour may be indicative of specific chakra dysfunction.

Healing through sound

Ancient healing traditions reflect the recognition that images and thoughts are not the only psychic mediators of energy, but that sound is too. This understanding forms the basis for the use of sound in healing.

Sounds are different qualities of vibration, and as such are characteristically associated with different energies within the body, which is why the profoundly deaf may be competent musicians or have a sophisticated musical appreciation. The mantras or sounds used in the meditation traditions of India were considered by the ancients to have definite physical effects. Indeed, in ancient religious traditions throughout the world sound was recognised as having the power to heal or destroy. The fighting cry of the Japanese Samurai warriors, when uttered in a minor key, is said to produce a reaction that is quite literally stunning in that it lowers arterial blood pressure so suddenly that it produces partial paralysis.

Modern science utilises the same principles, high-frequency

sound-waves being employed in ultrasound treatments and diagnosis, while at the other extreme very-high-frequency sound-waves are being explored as a military weapon.

Sound therapies attempt to harness sound-waves in the diagnosis and treatment of disease. They have a very long history, even in Western culture, where they were first developed by the Ancient Egyptians and Greeks. Music therapy is well established and regarded as effective in the treatment and management of the mentally handicapped and disturbed adolescents. Its main effects are generally considered to relate to the promotion of relaxation – and for this reason it is widely used in so-called relaxation tapes – but it may also have direct influences on specific organs and areas of the body. Meditation using sounds traditionally associated with the chakras, either chanted or rehearsed mentally, may therefore be beneficial.

Healing with plant energies

Herbalism

Most people are aware that medicines originate in the plant world, morphine being derived from the poppy, cocaine from the leaves of the coca plant, digitalis from the foxglove, and so on. Numerous other remedies are essentially herbal preparations. Herbalism, one of the highly refined arts of the shaman, has been established throughout the world since the earliest times and modern scientific research is confirming much of the ancient wisdom of the herbalist. Some rediscovered or more recently developed remedies that have been dismissed merely as 'fads' by many orthodox medical practitioners and laymen alike are also being recognised as highly effective alternatives to conventional medications. For example, there is increasing research evidence that dietary support with evening primrose oil is effective in ameliorating the clinical signs of atopic eczema and other allergic skin diseases for which the normal treatment involves drugs and hyposensitisation procedures that incur significant risks of side-effects, and may not be effective (Curds, 1990).

Indeed, the National Health Service has now granted permission to doctors to prescribe evening primrose oil for people suffering from allergic dermatitis, and this treatment is producing some excellent results. Research being conducted by the Royal Veterinary College into the use of evening primrose oil in the treatment of canine and feline allergic skin diseases and idiopathic pruritis is confirming these findings and resulting in a marked reduction of clinical signs of disease.

Plant essences

Throughout history certain plant essences have been regarded as acting at a more profound level than merely the physical. Flowers have been used worldwide as symbols of humanity's higher spiritual faculties and adopted as emblems of religious and spiritual movements. The Tibetan tradition teaches of a direct link betwen man's unconscious mind and the plant kingdom, and claims that man has the ability to contact his own essential nature or soul at an unconscious level through plants, and so restore harmony within himself. A similar view is held in many ancient cultures, but it was put forward in more recent times by Dr Edward Bach, an eminent Harley Street physician, who developed the Flower Remedies that bear his name during the first half of this century. He distinguished between plants that relieve physical symptoms and those that influence the spiritual aspects of man and may be used to treat incipient illness before it manifests in the physical body.

Bach's system is similar to homeopathy in recognising physical illness as symptomatic of spiritual dis-ease, which he viewed as a distortion of the energy field of the body resulting in negative 'soul' states that correspond to various flower remedies. Flower remedies could therefore be used to re-establish harmonious frequencies and vibrations, and so the balance of energies within the body. The remedies, operating at subtle energy levels through the principle of resonance, thus act as a catalyst for regeneration. The mental outlook of the patient is seen as an indication of the necessary remedy, because Bach believed that the mind shows the onset and course of disease more definitely than the body.

Bach's remedies, together with diagnostic charts, are widely available in health stores and are used by many healers who diagnose the appropriate remedies for their clients. However, self-diagnosis and treatment are often more reliable, as the individual can generally recognise characteristic mental states and attitudes more accurately than another person, although this is not always the case. Once again, cues to the appropriate remedies can invariably be divined from the content of imagery, either that generated by a healer in response to a client or that produced by the individual in dreams, reverie or fantasy. I have found that when a plant or tree features powerfully or repeatedly in a person's imagery they invariably derive very definite benefits from the corresponding Bach Remedy, or from the plant essences used in aromatherapy.

Aromatherapy

The effect of odours on the emotions has been recognised for many centuries. The therapeutic application of this understanding – aromatherapy – originated in Ancient Egypt. It flourished in the Greek and Roman empires, but with their collapse went into a decline and practically disappeared until it resurfaced during the last century. In Britain it is regarded by most people merely as an adjunct to the cosmetic industry, but in continental Europe it is widely employed in orthodox medicine. French physicians, for example, routinely administer aromatherapy oils alongside more conventional medications. Oils such as lavender and clove have long been employed for their analgesic effects, camphor and eucalyptus as decongestants, fennel, basil and thyme as aids to digestion; and ti tree, given by Aborigines to Captain Cook's sick crew, is now recognised as being a highly potent antibacterial, antifungal and antibiotic agent.

What are termed 'fragrant essential oils' are employed in aromatherapy, and applied to the body through massage. Research has shown that, as used in therapy, these oils have beneficial psychological effects, notably in the treatment of depression and anxiety, and have useful applications in the treatment of anxiety-related physical conditions such as travel-sickness and indigestion.

Studies conducted at the University of Cincinnatti (reported in *New Scientist*, 2 March 1991) have found that people perform much better in tasks requiring sustained attention when they are given regular whiffs of peppermint. Peppermint has also been investigated at the Catholic University of America in Washington, DC, where it has been found that the brain-wave patterns in subjects treated with the fragrance are those associated with alertness, and that the fragrance enhances the sensory pathway for visual detection, allowing subjects more control over their allocation of attention. The effects of fragrances are also being investigated at the Rensselaer Polytechnic Institute in New York State. Thinking, mood and behaviour have all been found to be significantly affected when fragrances are introduced into working environments.

Thus, despite relatively little definitive evidence on the effectiveness of aromatherapy, it is being used in a number of settings. At the Memorial Sloan-Kettering Hospital in New York fragrances are being wafted into a body scanner to calm patients, while in Japan fragrances are being blown into the atmosphere to keep workers busy or relaxed, depending on their jobs and the time of day. The Kajima Corporation in Tokyo is reported as favouring the use of citrus in the morning, floral fragrances at midday and woodland scents in the afternoon.

The most recent approach to aromatherapy focuses on the essential oils not as chemical mixtures but as liquid vibrations, each having a certain resonance corresponding with specific bodily organs and thus with sound and colour, which can be used in much the same way to treat disease at a subtle energy level.

Healing through shapes and symbols

The essential materialism or physicialism of Western culture often makes it difficult for those raised within it to accept what are fundamentally ancient spiritual views and their applicability to modern therapeutic practice. Those who may accept, however grudgingly, that colour, sound and even scents have vibrational qualities that may produce physiological effects are often unable to comprehend that shapes and symbols can have similar effects. They may therefore dismiss their possible significance in diagnosis and treatment.

Traditional healers or shamans, however, placed considerable reliance on them, and visualisation of and meditation upon shapes and symbols are important features of many healing practices. In the Indian tradition each chakra is associated with a symbolic shape: the base chakra with a square, the second chakra with a pyramid with the capstone removed, the solar plexus chakra with a circle or sphere, the heart chakra with an equilateral cross, the throat chakra with a chalice, the brow chakra with a six-point star and the crown chakra with the thousand-petalled lotus flower. Meditation on these is held to be a means of stimulating and balancing the energies of each centre. Similar symbols are thought to be represented on the totem poles of Native North Americans and in the iconography of many other peoples. However, perhaps through lack of understanding of their significance as energy transformers, many Westerners have little affinity with these symbols and often find them difficult to use in meditation and visualisation.

Animal symbolism is also a common feature of most ancient traditions and shamans typically make use of so-called 'power animals' in their treatments. For many Westerners animal symbolism and imagery has greater potency than the inanimate symbols of the Eastern traditions, and so a method has been developed by an American psychotherapist, Eligio Gallegos, which uses the former. He claims that this method produces metaphoric descriptions related to the chakra system in a form readily understandable to the Western client and therapist, and that it can serve as both a vivid diagnostic tool and a medium for effecting therapy and growth. The following exercise is based on that developed by Gallegos (1983).

Exercise 11
Developing insight into the chakra system through animal imagery

Sitting or lying comfortably with eyes closed, proceed to relax in whatever way you find most effective.

When you feel relaxed, focus your attention on the base of your spine and become aware of all the feelings and sensations in that area. Then allow those feelings to transform into the image of an animal. Allow this to occur spontaneously and do not attempt to choose an image consciously or to censor any image that arises.

When you have identified the animal, observe what it is doing. Ask it whether it has a name, and if you are uncertain as to what it is doing, ask it to explain its actions. Then ask if it has anything to tell or teach you at this time. Pay close attention to its response, and remember that this may be in the form of signs or symbols rather than a verbal message.

When you have taken note of its responses to your initial questions, ask if there is anything it needs or if there is anything you can do for it. Note how you respond to its replies and whether or not you feel inclined to act on them. Then ask the animal any other question that you feel is appropriate, before thanking the animal for presenting itself.

When you have done this, repeat the procedure by focusing in turn on the area just below your navel, and that just above it; then on the centre of your chest; on the centre of your throat; between and just above your eyebrows; and on the crown of your head.

Having done so, introduce the animals to each other and observe how they interrelate. Identify any tensions or conflicts that exist between different animals, and engage the assistance of them all in helping resolve these difficulties. Ask for their support in helping each one to achieve its full potential and for them all to work co-operatively and harmoniously.

Should you find that the feelings in any area spontaneously assume a form other than an animal, do not attempt to change it. Observe it closely, noting all its details, and attempt to establish the same dialogue as you would with the animal, asking its name, what it is doing, what you can learn from it and so on. If, with either the animal or non-animal images, you cannot establish any meaningful dialogue in words or pictures, then ask yourself what you believe is occurring in that area, what you can learn from it, and what you can do to be of assistance. Having done so, return to normal awareness and take some time to record your experience.

Commentary

This exercise often takes time and in workshops I suggest that participants keep their notebooks to hand so that they can record their observations of and 'conversations' with the various animals immediately. Some interrupt each phase of the exercise to do this, while others prefer to continue until the end before doing so.

Usually I precede the exercise with a fairly lengthy progressive relaxation, as I have found that many people, initially at least, find that tensions and sensations elsewhere distract from focus on the chakra areas. The success of the exercise depends to a great extent on how much the individual is able to let go of ordinary concerns, preoccupations and thought processes. Those who are insufficiently relaxed in this respect tend to find that the feelings in a given area do not easily transform into imagery and they either conclude that the exercise 'isn't working' or begin to impose animals consciously. Others may reject the animals that do arise spontaneously, and try to change them into those they would prefer. Both of these tendencies are meaningful and worth exploring, in that the animal someone seeks to impose in an area may represent how that person wishes the area to be, and the features of the animals that are rejected may reflect aspects of the self that the person does not wish to acknowledge, or various assumptions and attitudes that underpin the utilisation of these energies. As the aim of the exercise is to promote the harmonious integration of all the individual's energies, these negated or rejected features need to be addressed and assimilated. In some cases inability to imagine animals at any or all of the chakras may be an indication of resistance in that area and is worth exploring further. Similarly, negative responses to the information and/or requests obtained from the animals need to be examined more closely. However, failure to imagine an animal may simply be because it is not as appropriate an image as certain others, and for this reason I advise that the person should work with whatever image presents itself, however strange this may be. The most unusual reported so far was the slice of cherry tart that a man imagined floating on its side over his base chakra.

The base animal

Gallegos reports that the base or grounding animal is usually a sure-footed animal or one that lives close to the earth – such as a prairie dog, rabbit, goat, deer, antelope or kangaroo – and it is usually a beautifully supportive animal that may teach the person how to be at home with nature. While all these and many more are frequently encountered, I have found that the most commonly reported animals in relation to this chakra are cats, both domestic and wild such as lions, tigers and panthers; rhinos, hippos and large aquatic mammals such as whales; and snakes and dragons, whose power and vitality is unmistakable. These features are clearly important in relation to the functions of the base chakra energies in providing a firm basis to one's existence and a will to live. The serpent and dragon are, of course, respectively traditional Indian and Chinese symbols for the earthy energies located at the base of the spine.

Sometimes these base animals betray blockages in that area, as in the case of a young woman who imagined a hippo stuck in a tree-trunk, which was subsequently released by a beaver associated with a higher chakra who needed the wood. This was in itself interesting given that beavers are the animal world's master dam builders, and wherever they appear in association with chakra energies they are a good indication of blocked energies. Immobile animals at this site, however large, are suggestive of inefficient utilisation of energies. One man who was gratified by the secure base provided by a hippo was less content with the fact that it appeared to be lying in a shallow pool completely motionless, as if dead.

Other animals may also suggest dysfunction in the energies at the base chakra, for example weak animals or insects that are easily squashed or short lived, or animals that take flight. Rabbits are somewhat ambiguous in this respect and need careful investigation if their symbolic meaning is to be correctly interpreted. On the one hand they are ground-dwelling, highly reproductive animals; but on the other, as they live in burrows in the ground, they may suggest, quite literally, undergroundedness, and they are easily frightened, which may be an indication of fear and insecurity. Rabbits also tend to be very short lived, most of those living in the wild surviving only a year or less because of predators. Gallegos reports one of his clients whose base animal was a rabbit and whose other animals were large and powerful. The rabbit expressed a fear of the others because of their size and so, in the animal council subsequently imagined by the client, the other animals encouraged the rabbit to grow to be their equal, which it did, and no longer felt afraid and unsettled.

The 'gutsy' animal

Gallegos reports that the second-chakra animal, which relates to the gut and 'gut' feelings, frequently appears as large or spirited, and occasionally as restrained – a caged tiger, or a tethered or hobbled horse. Once again, this is not entirely borne out by my workshop experience. My observation of several hundred persons indicates that the 'gut' animals tend to be small rather than large, and very commonly (as opposed to occasionally) they are restrained in some way or inert. Many of the animals imagined are asleep (numerous people have apparently left 'sleeping dogs' to lie there), and dormice and other hibernating animals proliferate, as do sluggish creatures of every kind. This may, of course, be a very telling reflection on the British character, which could account for any differences noted between Gallegos' subjects and mine. Hamsters and squirrels have occurred on several occasions, suggesting energies being stored, and even lost, rather than utilised; and like other rodents they may be indicative of emotions 'gnawing away' at the person. One woman reported a mouse running 'the wrong way' around a wheel in an attempt to slow it down.

The solar plexus animal

Gallegos describes the solar plexus or power animal as highly individual, perhaps a stallion in need of taming, or a sleek panther. He notes that women often appear to have a power that is hidden, as is suggested by a raccoon, ostrich, or teddy bear (although I fail to see the latter as in any sense powerful, which just goes to show the importance of discovering the personal meanings of imagery). Certainly the most common animals in this area would appear to be large and powerful, with a preponderance of red-deer stags and reindeer, the British imagination seemingly having been shaped by Sir Edwin Landseer's portrayal of 'The Monarch of the Glen'. In contrast, rabbits and other characteristically fearful animals may appear, indicating anxiety, timidity, and submissiveness, although this can again be ambiguous as a kick from a rabbit can be very powerful indeed. Nevertheless, rabbits are generally easily overwhelmed.

The heart animal

Gallegos says of the heart animal that it '. . . has varied greatly and, in the few cases where there have been similarities, is a lion or a bear. Beyond this, individuality emerges: a fish in an intensely Catholic person, a dove in a peacemaker, a chicken in a young teenager afraid of his emerging passions.' This view is supported in my workshop experience, the animal symbols for love and compassion perhaps being more uniquely personal than others, and requiring close attention and scrutiny for that very reason. Some suggest dysfunction and may provide clues to difficulties in relationships. For example, a galloping horse, marauding elephant or bounding kangaroo may indicate an indifference to the feelings of others, and transient or hasty relationships, while a snake curled tightly around a branch may reveal a clinging, dependent tendency.

The throat animal

Gallegos suggests that the throat or communications animal is generally the least developed of all, frequently appearing as a snake, turtle or other primitive or defensive creature. This is certainly supported by my workshop experience, where very frequently indeed this animal is missing altogether, especially in women. Snakes are common, however, suggesting perhaps a tendency towards introjection, or swallowing whole the views and opinions of others, and

210

perhaps a tendency to 'speak with forked tongue' – to deceive and mislead rather than express the truth of oneself.

Gallegos observes that the animals in this exercise often grow in size or transform into a completely different animal, and that this growth has characteristically been followed by changes in the client's relationship to the environment in terms of thought, feeling and behaviour; and that the reverse is also true, with changes the client undergoes in everyday life being reflected in the animals and the relationship to each other. These changes may occur over time, or suddenly. He notes that the throat animal is usually one of the first animals to undergo growth and transformation, as people develop in their ability to express themselves and especially their true feelings. He suggests that the lack of development in this area is a cultural phenomenon, and that rather than not learning how to communicate, we learn how *not* to communicate.

The brow animal

The brow animal is frequently a bird, such as an eagle, owl or hawk, a large cat, or other strongly visual animal. Heightened sensitivities are possibly indicated in the image of a bat, although, depending on its behaviour, it could also be interpreted as dormant, and therefore reflect that the chakra is unopened and in need of energising.

The crown animal

Gallegos reports that his work on exploring the spiritual or crown chakra has been minimal, largely because he omits it from his exercise (for reasons that he does not explain). I have found that few people have difficulty with this image and many are quite excited by it. Spiders at the centre of their webs, suggesting interconnectedness and radiating outwards, or birds flying overhead, indicative of transcendence, are not uncommonly reported; but perhaps the most common image for this chakra is the snake, which may be an indication that in many people it is relatively undeveloped.

211

Gallegos comments on the intensity of feeling and emotion that these imaginary animals evoke and of the deep warmth and support that is felt from them. He observes that this is a characteristic feature of visualisation in general, because feelings are much closer to images than they are to words and verbal thought-processes.

While this is certainly true, and many people feel great affection for their animals, it is also true that they can be quite disturbed by them, especially where an animal is trapped or distressed. One person reported seeing at her solar plexus chakra a huge bison standing as though just in front of a movie camera and swaying rhythmically like a caged zoo animal. Initially she could make little sense of this image, until she withdrew in her mind's eye to a more distant vantage point. Then the bison could be seen to be cut off from the remainder of the herd by an open geological faultline that was too wide and deep to cross. The bison was eventually led to safety and restored to the herd. This, and similar imagery which reveals a separation of some kind, is possibly indicative of the need for healing of that centre. In this case, it suggests that the woman's energies were cut off through her own 'fault'.

Gallegos indicates that one exciting aspect of this exercise is that people are well able to observe *where* a difficulty occurs. They can not only gain insight into the nature of that difficulty and its implications for other aspects of themselves, but can marshall their energies in order to overcome it. As a result it is not unusual for significant changes to occur in a single session. Certainly this exercise, as a culmination of a series of exercises, has led to dramatic transformations in health, both psychological and physical, and lifestyle. It is not, however, an exercise particularly well suited to inexperienced visualisers, and is best preceded by the previous chakra exercise, which sensitises people to these energies.

A final word

Participants in my workshops are always provided with the opportunity to sense physically or objectively the chakras, auras and energies of others. This allows them to explore their sensitivity, both physical and psychic, to subtle forces at work not only in and around them but in others. Exercises in resisting and overcoming energies in others are performed, together with those that involve channelling energies to others for healing.

These exercises have not been included here because the focus of the exercises within this book is on self-healing, which is the necessary precedent and ongoing accompaniment to healing others. The book therefore ends where it commences, with the wisdom of the ancients and their fundamental premise that the healer must first heal himself, and can do so through relaxation and imagery, or imaginative medicine.

REFERENCES AND FURTHER READING

Achterberg, J., Simonton, S.M. and Simonton, O.C. (1977), 'Psychology of the exceptional cancer patients: a description of patients who outlive predicted life expectancies', *Psychotherapy: Theory, Research and Practice*, 14, 4, Winter, pp.416–22.

Achterberg, J. and Lawlis, G.F. (1978), *Imagery of Cancer*, Champaign, Illinois, Institute for Personality and Testing.

Achterberg, J. (1985), *Imagery in Healing: Shamanism and Modern Medicine*, Boston and London, New Science Library, Shambhala.

Ahmedazi, S. (1987), 'Pet Therapy', *Pedigree Digest*, vol.13, no.4, p.11.

Bach, E. (1986), *The Twelve Healers and Other Remedies*, Frome, Somerset, Hillman.

Bahnson, C.B. (1976), 'Emotional and personality characteristics of cancer patients', *Oncologic Medicine*, A. Sutuick (ed.), University Park Press.

Benson, H.D. and Zlipper, M.Z. (1975), *The Relaxation Response*, London, Collins.

Birren, F. (1978), *Color and Human Response*, New York, Van Nostrand Reinhold.

Blakeslee, T. (1980), *The Right Brain: A New Understanding of the Unconscious Mind and its Powers*, London, MacMillan.

Boadella, D. (1987), *Lifestreams: An Introduction to Biosynthesis*, London, Routledge.

Brohn, P. (1986), *Gentle Giants*, London, Century.

Broverman, J.K., Broverman, D.M., Clarkson, F.E., Rosenkrantz, P.S. and Vogel, S.R. (1970), 'Sex role stereotypes and clinical judgments of mental health', *Journal of Consulting and Clinical Psychology*, no.34, pp.1–7.

Brown, G.W. and Harris, T. (1978), *Social Origins of Depression: A Study of Psychiatric Disorder in Women*, London, Tavistock Publications.

Butler, W.E. (1987), *How to Read the Aura*, London, Aquarian.

Charlesworth, E.A. and Nathan, R.G. (1987), *Stress Management*, London, Transworld Publishers Ltd.

Cleary, B. (1988), 'Rachel's Story', *Caduceus*, no.4, p.5.

Cousins, N. (1981), *Anatomy of an Illness as Perceived by the Patient: Reflections on Healing and Regeneration*, New York and London, Bantam.

Curds, P. (1990), 'Not up to scratch', *Kennel Gazette*, vol.CXII, no.1321, pp.60–65, Dorchester, Friary Press.

Doore, G. (ed.) (1988), *Shaman's Path: Healing, Personal Growth and Empowerment*, Boston and London, Shambhala.

Dossey, L. (1982), *Space, Time and Medicine*, Boston and London: Shambhala.

Editorial (1987), 'Health benefits of pets: the first medical symposium on companion animals, *Pedigree Digest*, vol.14, no.1, p.5.

Editorial (1991), 'On the scent of a better day at work', *New Scientist*, 2 March, p.18.

Friedman, M. and Rosenham, R.H. (1974), *Type A Behaviour and Your Heart*, New York, Alfred A. Knopf.

Gallegos, E.S. (1983), 'Animal imagery, the chakra system and psychotherapy', *Journal of Transpersonal Psychology*, vol.15, no.2, pp.125–136.

Gillespie, J. (1989), *Brave Heart*, London, Century.

Gimbel, T. (1978), *Healing Through Colour*, Saffron Walden, C.W. Daniels.

Gove, W.K. and Tudor, J. (1972), 'The relationship between sex roles, marital status and mental illness', *Social Forces*, 51, 34.

Graham, H. (1990), *Time, Energy and the Psychology of Healing*, London, Jessica Kingsley.

Harner, M. (1990), *The Way of the Shaman: A Guide to Power and Healing*, New York, Harper and Row.

Harrison, J. (1984), *Love Your Disease: It's Keeping You Healthy*, London, Angus & Robertson.

Hewitt, J. (1982), *The Complete Relaxation Book: A manual of Eastern and Western Techniques*, London, Rider.

Hewitt, L. (1986), 'Women and Drugs', paper presented at the annual Conference of the Standing Conference on Drug Abuse, York University.

Howell, E. and Baynes, M. (eds.) (1981), *Women and Mental Health*, New York, Basic Books.

Hughes, H. and Molloy, F. (1990), 'Type A behaviour and attitude towards coping strategies when faced with stress', unpublished dissertation submitted in fulfilment of the requirement for B.A. (Hons) Psychology, Keele University.

Inglis, B. (1987), *The Unknown Guest: The Mystery of Intuition*, London, Chatto and Windus.

Ivanov, A. (1965), 'Soviet experiments in eyeless vision', *International Journal of Parapsychology*, vol.1, pp.5–22.

Jacobsen, C.F. (1929), 'Electrical measurements of neuro-muscular states during mental activities: imagination involving skeletal muscle', *American Journal of Physiology*, no.91, pp.597–608.

Jacobsen, E. (1938), *Progressive Relaxation*, University of Chicago Press.

Jacobsen, E. (1977), *You Must Relax*, London, Souvenir Press.

Jampolsky, G.G. (1979), *Love is Letting Go Of Fear*, Berkeley, California, Celestial Arts.

LeShan, L. (1989), *Cancer as a Turning Point: A Handbook for People with Cancer, Their Families and Health Professionals*, Bath, Gateway Books.

Lichstein, K.L. and Lipshitz, Z.E. (1982), 'Psychophysiological effects of noxious imagery', *Behaviour Research and Therapy*, no.20, pp.339–345.

Llewelyn, S. (1981), 'Psychology and women: an examination of mental health problems', *Bulletin of the British Psychological Society*, no.34, pp.60–63.

MacLaine, S. (1989) *Going Within: A Guide for Inner Transformation*, New York and London, Bantam.

Manning, M. (1989), *Matthew Manning's Guide to Self-Healing*, London, Thorsons.

Maslow, A. (1966), *Toward a Psychology of Being*, New York, Van Nostrand Reinhold.

Melzack, P. (1973), *The Puzzle of Pain*, London, Penguin.

Moon, T. and Moon, H. (1984), 'Hypnosis and childbirth: self-report and comment', *British Journal of Clinical Hypnosis*, 1, 49–52.

Naish, P.L.N. (ed.) (1986), *What is Hypnosis? Current Theories and Research*, Milton Keynes, Open University Press.

Oaklander, V. (1978), *Windows to our Children: A Gestalt Therapy Approach to Children and Adolescents*, Utah, Real People's Press.

Ostrander, I.S. and Schroeder, L.S. (1973), *Psychic Discoveries Behind the Iron Curtain*, London, Sphere Books.

Pelletier, K. (1978), *Mind as Slayer, Mind as Healer*, London, Allen & Unwin.

Penfold, P.S. and Walker, G.A. (1984), *Woman and the Psychiatric Paradox*, Milton Keynes, Open University Press.

Perls, F.S. (1976), *The Gestalt Approach and Eye Witness to Therapy*, London, Bantam.

Price, S. (1987) *Practical Aromatherapy: How to Use Essential Oils and Restore Vitality*, London, Thorsons.

Richardson, M. (1988), 'Medicine Now', BBC Radio 4, 14 October.

Roet, B. (1988), Address given at the World Health Day, Holistic Health Centre, Farnham, April.

Roney-Dougal, S.M. (1989), 'The psychophysiology of the yogic chakra system', *Caduceus* no.8, pp.8–11.

Scarlett, C. (1987), 'Helping pets help the aged', *Pedigree Digest*, vol.14, no.1, pp.5 and 11.

Schultz, J.H. and Luthe, W. (1961), 'Autogenic Training', *Proceedings of the Third International Congress of Psychiatry*, Montreal.

Schwartz, J. (1980), *Human Energy Systems*, New York, E.P. Dutton.

Shaw, W.A. (1946), 'The relaxation of muscular action potentials to imaginal weightlifting', *Archives of Psychology*, 247, 250.

Siegel, B.S. (1986), *Love, Medicine and Miracles*, London,

Rider.

Siegel, B.S. (1990), *Peace, Love and Healing*, London, Rider.

Simonton, O.C., Matthews-Simonton, S., and Creighton, J.L. (1988), *Getting Well Again: A Step-By-Step Self-Help Guide to Overcoming Cancer for Patients and Their Families*, New York and London, Bantam.

Steinbrecher, E.C. (1988), *The Inner Guide Meditation: A Primer for the 21st Century*, London, Aquarian.

Stern, J.A., Brown, M., Ulet, G.H. and Stellen, I. (1977), 'A comparison of hypnosis, acupuncture, morphine, valium, aspirin and placebo in the management of experimentally induced pain', *Annals of NY Academy of Science*, 296, pp.175–193.

Totton, N. and Edmondson, E. (1988), *Reichian Bodywork: Melting the Blocks to Life and Love*, Dorset, England, Prism Press.

Trechman, E.J. (translator, undated), *The Essays of Montaigne*, Oxford University Press.

Vollmar, K. (1987), *Journey Through the Chakras*, Bath, Gateway Books.

Webster, C. (1988), 'The 19th century after-life of Paracelsus' in R. Cooper (ed.) *Studies in the History of Alternative Medicine*, pp. 79–88, MacMillan.

West, M. (1979), 'Meditation', *British Journal of Psychiatry*, no. 135, pp.457–69.

West, M. (1980), 'Meditation and the EEG', *Psychological Medicine*, no.10, pp.369–75.

Whyte, A.M. (1987), 'Pets in prisons', *Pedigree Digest*, vol.13, no.4, pp.10–11.

Wilson, A. and Bek, L. (1987), *What Colour Are You? The Way to Health through Colour*, London, Aquarian.

Wood, B. (1987), *The Healing Power of Colour*, London, Aquarian.

Young, J. (1990), 'Meridians, chakras and psychic abilities: the work of Hiroshi Motoyama', *Caduceus*, no.10, pp.9–13.

INDEX

Achterberg, Jeanne 137
acupuncture and
   acupressure ix, 33, 145,
   183–4, 195
adenosine triphosphate 35
adrenalin 30, 32, 179
aggression 54, 92, 109, 140
agoraphobia ix, 94, 98
AIDS 8
Aikado 178, 183, 195
alcohol 10, 31, 37, 90, 92,
   128, 197
Alexander, Franz 124
Alexander Technique 196
Alixithymia 55, 123
Allen, Woody 156
allergies viii, 31, 202
amnesia 60
anaesthesia 60, 184
anger 54, 140, 155–6, 194
animal imagery 22–3, 24,
   131, 171, 205–12
   exercise 206
Anma healing 183
anorexia nervosa 197, 199
anxiety and fear
   imagery exercise 112–13
   likely to shorten life 32,
      121
   and meditation 37
   neuroses 72–3, 74, 92, 94

produced by imagination
   6–8, 11, 19, 112, 120
as self-defence 105–6,
   133, 194
tendency to rationalise
   80–1, 91, 103
tendency to repress 46,
   99–101, 106–7, 113–
   19
in terminally ill 111
ways to allay viii, 60, 98,
   107, 112–19, 149, 204
aromatherapy ix, 203–4
arteriosclerosis 11
arthritis, rheumatoid viii,
   31, 39, 55, 56, 90–1,
   128, 133
Assagioli, Roberto 75, 164–5
asthma 11, 36, 55, 60
attitudinal healing 110
audiotapes: aids to
   relaxation x, 26, 201
auras and auric vision 180–
   2, 184, 187, 189, 200
Autogenic Training 146

Bach, Edward, and Bach
   Remedy 202–3
back problems 14–15, 31,
   60, 144
bedwetting 60

Benson, Herbert 38, 40
Berke, Joseph 72–3
blindness and colour vision
    197–8
blood
    high pressure 6, 10, 30,
        31, 32
    lowering pressure 11, 23,
        36, 60, 121
    sugar and other content
        levels 6, 30, 108, 110,
        121, 178
    vasolidation 17, 122
Boadella, David 193–5
brain
    cerebral haemorrhage 52
    effects of relaxation 36,
        144
    functioning 2, 51–4, 55–
        6, 60, 122–3, 151
    stroke 6, 30, 52–3
brain see also nervous
    system
breathing
    in exercises 17, 24, 40
    and laughter 110
    and meditation 36, 38, 49
    under tension 10, 30,
        144, 193
breathing see also T'ai Chi
Bristol Cancer Help Centre
    129
burn injuries 128, 145
buttocks 14, 144

cancer
    breast 54, 74, 123–4, 156
    'deadly' image 7–8, 155
    imagery and treatment
        60, 74, 126–9, 130–1,
        136–8, 149, 172, 190,
        197
    link with emotion 54, 56,
        90, 123–4, 156
    pain 142–3, 145
    stress effects 31, 39, 109,
        126
catharsis 20
Catholic University of
    America 204
chakra system 177–81, 184,
    187–90, 193–5, 196,
    201, 205, 206–12
chemotherapy 60, 111, 128,
    136
Chinese healing traditions
    178, 182–4, 208
cholesterol levels 6
Christianity 3–4, 106, 110,
    159
Churchill, Sir Winston 160–1
Cincinatti University 204
clairvoyance ix, 3, 4, 56,
    177, 179, 200
colitis 11, 55
colour imagery and therapy
    44–5, 67–8, 181, 188–9,
    196–200, 204, 205
constipation 31
convulsions 11
coughing 11
Cousins, Norman 110
cystic fibrosis ix

daemonic influence 159–61
Dante Alighieri 159
death 32, 111, 121, 135
de Bono, Edward 95
dentistry 60, 111, 141, 146
depression 54, 67, 92–3,

94, 194
SAD 199
ways to relieve viii, 60,
172, 197, 199, 203
dermatitis, allergic 202
diabetes 11, 31
Do-in healing 183, 195
doctors: patients'
relationship with 9
Dossey, Larry 108
dreams
daydreams and fantasies
57, 78, 118–19, 125,
163, 164
guided fantasy exercises
77, 78–87, 165–70
interpretation xi, 4, 43,
57, 68, 162
nightmares 92, 191
drugs
abuse 31, 92
analgesic 33, 145
sedative 11, 91, 145, 155
dyslectics 53

Eastern culture 52, 89, 110,
137, 159, 200, 208
healing practices 37, 110,
177–80, 182–4, 195,
202, 205
eczema, atopic 201
Egypt, Ancient 3, 9–10,
177, 196, 201, 203
Einstein, Albert 35, 161
emotion
brain processes 122–5
catharsis 20
in *chakra* system 179,
190–1, 212
difference in sexes 71–2,

89–92
emotional pain 142–3,
152–7
and imagery 140
link with illness 54–6,
72–4, 109, 123–5, 126,
155, 192–3
Empedocles 3
encephalitis, myalgic viii
endocrine system 178, 189,
199
endorphins 60, 110, 143,
144–5
energy
auric field 180–2
chakra and other Eastern
concepts 177–80, 182–
4, 187–93, 195, 208
energy imagery exercise
40–1
Freud and Jung theories
161–3
in physics 34–5, 49, 176
sensing exercise 185–91
submerged and potential
40–50, 176
and time 33–6
vibration patterns 49,
182, 184–5, 204
epilepsy 53
expectation 97–103, 108–
10, 114, 136, 170

face
in *chakra* and auras 179,
181, 194, 210–11
exercises 16–17, 144
fantasies *see* dreams
fatigue 11, 179
fear *see* anxiety and fear

221

Feldenkrais Method 196
food
  digestion 11, 179, 190
  effects of meditation 37
  overeating 31, 60, 95
food *see also* herbs
Frankl, Victor 75
Freud, Sigmund 20, 43, 57, 91, 105, 161–2, 164

Gallegos, Eligio 205–12 *passim*
gastro-intestinal problems viii, 6–7, 11, 30, 90, 121
genito-urinary problems 190
Gillespie, Joanne 136, 138
goitre, toxic 11
Greece, Ancient 3, 9–10, 75, 88–9, 196, 201, 203

Hahnemann, Samuel 184
Hammersmith Hospital, London 129
headaches *see also* migraine viii, 60, 144
heart
  in *chakra* concept 179, 194, 195, 210
  heart attack 6–7, 32, 39, 90
  heart rate 6, 15, 23, 32, 121, 179
  and laughter 110–11
  palpitations 11, 120
  stress related to disease 30, 109
Heisenberg, Werner 161
Heraclitus 3
herbs and herbalism ix, 3, 201–4

Hippocrates 3
HIV 8
hives 55
homeopathic medicine ix, 184–5, 202
hormone levels 6, 108, 121, 178, 199
housework: cause of stress 73, 76, 93, 94
hydrocortisones 30
hypertension *see also* stress; tension viii, 11, 30, 36
hypnosis ix, 10, 58–61, 145–6, 147, 148, 162
  exercise 61–3
hypochrondria 11

imagery
  animal 22–3, 24, 131, 171, 205–12
  and brain function 51–4, 55–6, 122–3, 144, 151
  in cancer treatment 126–9, 130–1, 136–9
  in children 118–19
  colour 44–5, 67–8, 196–8
  energy sensing and exercise 179, 185–91
  exercise to confront pain 149–50, 151–2, 156–7
  hidden treasure exercise 96–102
  hypnotic induction and exercise 59–65, 162
  and immune system 138–40
  inner guide visualisation 165–75
  personalisation 41–8, 56–8, 67–9, 102, 137

physiological effects 120–5, 127, 130–4, 144–9, 151, 196
problems with 20, 58, 64–9, 156–7, 190–1, 194
in progressive relaxation exercise 13–24 *see also* imagination exercises
to relax mental inflexibility 40–1, 120, 125, 136–7
to relieve anxiety and fear 112–19, 125–6, 148, 203
imagination
brain function 52, 56, 142, 145
exercises 40–1, 61–3, 78–9, 96–7, 112–13, 129–30, 149–50, 168–9, 185–7, 206
important for health 5–9, 117–18, 120–1
immune system
auto-immune disease viii
chakra concept 179–190
effect of imagery 133, 134, 137–9
HIV 8
hormone levels 108
stress effects 31, 121, 126
Indian and Tibetan healing traditions 37, 110, 177–80, 182, 200, 202, 205
Inglis, Brian 160
Inner Guide visualisation 159–60, 165–75
insomnia viii, 11, 18, 26, 60, 92

insulin 30
International Meditation Society 37
intuition 158, 160, 161, 164, 165

Jacobsen, E. 34–5
James, William 105, 108, 112
Japanese healing traditions 178, 182–4, 195, 204
Joan of Arc 159–60
Jung, Carl 43–4, 57, 75, 162–4, 175

Kajima Corporation 204
Karagulla, Sheila 181
Keele University vii
kidney disease 6–7, 11, 30
Koestler Foundation 160

Laing, R.D. 75
laughter 110–11, 118
le Carré, John 104
leisure activities: importance 23, 28, 33, 57, 164, 173–4
leisure activities *see also* sport
leisure industry x
LeShan, Lawrence 156
light *see* colour
loneliness 23
Lorenz, Konrad 110
love 179, 194, 210
Lown, Bernard 8–9
Lüscher, Max, and Luscher Colour Test 199–200

Maclaine, Shirley 167–8
Maeterlink, Maurice 160

Maharishi Mahesh Yogi 37
Manning, Matthew 140, 150
mantras 49, 188, 200
    mantra yoga 182
marriage 87, 89, 93–5
Marvin, Lee 89
Maslow, Abraham 70–1, 105, 106, 107
meditation 36–8, 49, 146–7, 162, 188, 196, 201, 205
melatonin 199
Melzack, Ronald 141–2, 143, 152
Memorial Sloan-Kettering Hospital, NY 204
men
    anxiety and fear 115
    defences 106
    fewer on courses than women x, 92
    imagery compared to women 68–9, 98
    role maintenance 71–2, 89–90, 95, 116
    stress and mental health 21, 90–3
menstrual problems 31
mental see mind
mentally handicapped 8
metamorphic technique 183
migraine viii, 17, 30, 55, 144, 147–8
mind
    conscious and unconscious 161–5, 196
    Inner Guide visualisation 159–60, 165–75

mental illness 72–7, 91–5, 144, 163 see also anxiety; neurosis; stress; trauma
mental (in)flexibility 38–42, 64–7, 107, 109–10, 118, 125, 136–7, 170
Montaigne, Michel 120–1
moxibustion 183
multiple sclerosis viii, 31
muscles
    muscular tension 6, 10–12, 20, 30, 34–5, 121, 144
    muscle armouring 193–5
    ways to relax 13–18, 121, 145, 151, 193, 197
music therapy ix, 201
Myers, Frederick 161

nationality in self-actualisation 88
needs and wants 76–87
    exercise 78–9
neonatal jaundice 197
nephritis 11
nervous system
    in chakra concept 179
    disorders 11, 53–4, 55–6, 73, 179
    influence of imagery 125, 147
    nervous breakdown see mind; neuroses
    neuro-surgery 53, 141
    and pain 141–2
nervous system see also brain
neuroses 72–4, 91, 94, 153,

190, 192
Newton, Sir Isaac 34–5, 161
nightmares 92, 191

Oaklander, Violet 118
Oakley, Ann 76
OM concept 49

pain
  emotional 142–3, 152–7
  exercise to confront 149–
    50
  functional use 143, 150–
    1, 152
  nature of 8, 141–3, 146–7
  as punishment 147–9
  referred 14, 130–1
  relation with time 33,
    145
  ways to control 60, 110,
    128–9, 134, 141, 143–
    57, 171
Paracelsus 4
Pauli, Wolfgang 161, 165
Perls, Frederick 71–2, 76,
    81
pets 23
phobias viii, ix, 36, 72, 94,
    98, 119
pineal gland 179, 199
pituitary gland 179
placebos 9, 108, 145
Planck, Max 161
plants
  essences 202–3
  imagery 62–8
plants see also herbs
play: value of 117–18
Poincaré, Jules 161
primrose oil 201–2

psoriasis 197
psychiatry 76
psychology
  psychological medicine
    vii–viii, 20, 75, 108–9,
    111, 128–9, 143
  pain as psych. product 8,
    147, 152
  psych. function of
    imagery 125–6, 127,
    185, 187, 197–9
  psych. needs viii, 71, 76,
    88, 118, 191
  psychosomatic 164–5,
    192
  use of chakra 195
psychosomatic disorders 55,
    56, 71, 73
  psych. medicine 20, 124
psychotherapy 75, 76, 77,
    163–4
pulse rate 6, 10
Pythagoras 3

Rabindranath Tagore 172
radiotherapy 111, 128
reflexology ix, 33, 183, 195
Reich, Wilhelm 20, 192–3
Reiki healing 183
relaxation
  aids to x, 26–7, 49, 201
  exercises 12–18, 40–1,
    61–3, 78–9, 149–50,
    168–9
  flexibility of mental
    habits 38–40
  in guided fantasy exercise
    78
  and healing approaches
    33, 112, 195

under hypnosis 59–63,
    145–6
importance and nature of
    9–12, 18–23, 25, 110,
    122
meditation 36–7, 38,
    146–7
for pain control 143–5,
    148–51
prescribed for various
    complaints 11, 126–9
sense of time 19, 23–4,
    28–31, 35
religion *see also* Christianity
    88–9, 159, 170–1, 200
Rensselaer Polytechnic
    Institute 204
responsibility: tendency to
    evade 42–3, 73, 74, 103,
    107, 135–6
Roet, Brian 119, 147, 148

SAD (Seasonal Affective
    Depression) 199
schizophrenia 8
Schrödinger, Erwin 161
Schulz, Johannes 146
sex and sexuality 121, 160,
    161, 193–4, 197
shamans 4–5, 158–9, 164,
    189, 201
    use of imagery 9–10, 77,
        120, 126, 149, 205
Shiatsu 183, 195
Siegel, Bernie 8–9, 103,
    111, 124, 135, 166–7
Simonton(-Atchley), Carl
    and Stephanie 7, 126–7,
    129, 137–9, 165–9, 171,
    172

skin complaints viii, 31, 60,
    121, 197, 201
sleep *see also* dreams;
    insomnia 11, 25–6, 33,
    103–4
smoking 31, 37, 60
Socrates 159
solar plexus 181, 190, 194,
    195, 209–10, 212
sound therapy 49, 182, 188,
    200–1, 204, 205
speech 30, 52–3
Sperry, Roger 165
spirituality ix, 76, 88–9,
    170–1, 177, 187, 191
sport *see also* leisure
    activities 69, 112, 142,
    145
stomach *see also* food 15,
    17, 190
stress
    chakra concept 179
    in children 119
    and meditation 36–7
    men and women
        compared 21, 90–5
    psychological factors 109,
        190, 193
    related diseases 6–7, 39,
        72, 90–1, 128
    stressors in the
        imagination 6–8, 21–2
    time stress 28–31, 33–5
stress *see also* anxiety;
    hypertension;
    tension; trauma
stroke *see* brain
stuttering 11
subconscious *see* mind
suicide 109

surgery
  benefits of relaxation and imagery 11, 128
  neuro-surgery 53, 141
  preferred to change of lifestyle 103
  use of acupuncture 184
  use of hypnosis 60–1, 145
Swedenborg, Emanuel 161

T'ai Chi 33, 178, 183, 195, 196
TCP, cyclic 35
teeth see also dentistry 17, 144
telepathy 3, 4, 161
tension
  and imagery 127, 134
  pain caused by 151
  signs of 10, 72, 172
tension see also anxiety; hypertension; muscles; stress
therapy
  aromatherapy ix, 203–4
  bioenergetic 33
  chemotherapy 60, 111, 128, 136
  colour 196–200: 205 see also colour imagery
  Freud's theory 162
  music ix, 201
  psychotherapy 75, 76, 77, 163–4
  radiotherapy 111, 128
  sound therapy 49, 182, 188, 200–1, 204, 205
  zone therapy 183
Tibet see India and Tibet

time
  disease, pain and death 32–3, 145
  relationship with energy 33–6
  sense of time when relaxing 19, 23–4, 28
  time friendly/time conflicted people (Type A/B) 28–31, 33–5, 38, 56, 90
tinnitus ix, 153
Transcendental Meditation (TM) 37–8, 49
trauma 119, 128, 193
tsubo see acupuncture
tuberculosis 11

UCLA Medical School Pain Clinic 171
ulcers viii, 6–7, 11, 30, 60, 90, 179
ultrasound treatment 201

vertigo 31
veterinary medicine 185, 202
vibrational patterns 49, 182, 184–5, 188, 200–1, 204

Wall, Patrick 142, 143, 152
wants and needs 76–87
  exercise 78–9
witches 4–5
women
  imagery compared to men 68–9, 98, 101, 209, 210
  more on courses than

men x, 92

pregnancy and birth
  problems viii, 31, 143,
  145, 184, 190, 197,
  199

relations with children
  74, 114, 135–6, 154–5,
  156, 190–1

role maintenance 71–2,
  90–1, 92–5, 106

stress and mental health
  21, 91–3, 115, 191

work 34

yoga 33, 178, 182, 195

zone therapy 183